rescue from **house gorgeous**

rescue from
house gorgeous

SALVATION FROM HOUSE, FOOD & GARDEN PERFECTION

dan ho

RESCUEPRESS

A **RESCUE**PRESS Book
www.rescuepress.com

Library of Congress Control Number: 2004093988

First Edition

Acknowledgements: This book is based on my life, but the memorable
situations and interchangeable individuals in it are not at all the same as
the regrettable situations and wretched individuals who were actually
there. Therefore, those events and individuals are entirely fictitious. Jen
(and her eponymous restaurant), my mother, Muhammad Ali, Stanley
Tigerman, Aimee, Blanche, Marie, my dogs, and the French club chairs
are the gorgeous exceptions. Any resemblances to the actual are
entirely coincidental and can be attributed to my imagination working
overtime, which indicates that there's hope for the star-fuckers in
precious waterfront communities everywhere.

Book jacket images © RESCUEPRESS
Book design by Blue Design (www.bluedes.com)

ISBN Number 097557860X

Printed in Canada

Contents

Heaven holds a special place for Phyllis Mellman who suspected that my writing wasn't bad enough for do-it-yourself; for Pat Sims who helped me believe that Phyllis might just be right; for Lisa Dubrow for distinguishing life lived from life as written; for the 1992-1999 Lakeside staff who endured the epiphany; for the Rockwater Petes who gave uncalled-for respect; for Mom for her storytelling chops; for Dad for teaching manliness; and for Joe who never fails to reveal God.

FOR JENNY, WHO MATTERS THE MOST.

How to read this book

In this book, I will tell you that your dream home, whether it exists in your mind, on terra firma, or somewhere in between—say, on a blueprint or in a design contract, half-received in a warehouse and partially paid for on a credit card or with a second mortgage—is something you ought to seriously reconsider. I'm about to suggest that it is probably sucking the life out of you, and you've lost yourself in pursuit of the perfectly fluffed bank of pillows, cherry cabinets, cathedral ceilings, and cottage garden. In fact, I will say outright that you've disappeared while cleaning up after the atrocity of candles burned for ambient lighting, vanished while storing your pasta just so in someone's artistic fart in Mexican glass that you bought full price at Williams-Sonoma.

I realize that I may be preaching counter to the messages found on the very shelf on which you may have located this book, and that my message—yuck!—is a tough one which is quite un-focal-pointy, fabric-orgasmic, and *Provençal-s'il vous plait.* Truthfully, I cringe thinking that anyone would prescribe such a bitter pill without good reason, let alone sugar. (Dis my four-foot pot rack? What, are you crazy?) Even I wouldn't pick up that kind of book, decorator's nuisance that I am. But this is it: When the residence is refinanced (again) and all is said and done, I'm just a guy with a pretty house that overwhelmed him one day, who took the time to figure out why it did and set out trying to fix it.

As simple as the story and the lesson within sound, they don't translate well into the kind of book that you and I are used to seeing. Were this a classic how-to, pictures would neither serve nor enhance my personal notions of simplification without immediately, perhaps irrevocably, reducing them to misleading glossy images. Even the word "simple" evokes a minimalism that is not at all part of this book's efforts. Likewise, a straightforward narrative is no place for what I'm going to tell you about wire hangers and closet space. I'm nobody important enough to offer a memoir about housekeeping—is anybody? So instead I decided to give you a tale. And here we are.

In musical theater, the playwright defers to the composer when words fail to propel the story. In a Godard film, a reading of Mao Tse-tung pops up like seagull crap on your forehead when nothing flies overhead, and it works. In this book, narrative and prescription are like Torvill and Dean. I tried to separate them, God knows! In the end, I just had to get out the way and type so I could make myself useful.

As for motivation, I don't believe for a moment that the reasons you and I buy a table or choose a color of paint are limited to seeing them in a magazine or that some lifestyle guru demoed them on television. There are deeper stories attached to our decisions to acquire material possessions. I would be remiss if I attempted to fool you into believing that a list of projects in a handy book is reason enough for you to succeed in creating the home you hope is a dream come true. No way. You need to know the entire emotional reality before you can adopt my ideas to your good use.

So here it is: my how-to musical, my Godardian epic. Read liberally and apply as needed according to the directions.

STEP 1: ASSESS

CRAP • *n.* **1** *decorative domestic objects (vases, baskets, candlesticks, pillows) of no use other than to display or enhance same* **2** *artifacts that easily diminish in the absence of regular maintenance, augmentation, or seasonal reinvention* **3** *material things manufactured en masse that purport to evoke a different time, place, person, or nature* • *v. (crap up) to fill one's space with crap* • *adj. (crappy)* **1** *impulsive* **2** *unnecessary* **3** *redundant* **4** *contrived*

one

I was struck by lightning.

On February 12, 1998, I was thirty-two years old, married for almost seven strong years to Jenny, and by most accounts (at least those that mattered to me at the time), a fairly successful guy. I was by no means an Internet or Wall Street multimillionaire, but I was well-off enough. This is how I defined well-off at the time: Jenny and I (no partners) owned a small business that declared $250K annually in cash profit distinct from the allowable expenses of a Sub S corporation; we owned a large, custom-designed home with a sixty-foot pool. It was surrounded by two-plus acres of gardens, the annual upkeep of which could send a child to college. I'd think nothing of spending hundreds of dollars on a single tree, nor would Jenny flinch at her own petty extravagances.

We owned a restaurant, a good one, at least according to Zagat and others who make their living praising or trashing eateries. My card read "Owner/General Manager" and Jenny's, "Owner/Executive Chef." To many people this sounds like the ultimate job but, trust me, a whole lot of restaurateurs couldn't feel more different. I guess you could say I'm somewhere in between. I've always found it funny that we've all decided cooking and feeding are high art. Art lasts; you know what food becomes. I've read enough Beard, Child, and a buffet of recent cookbooks by the children of their food nation to nod eagerly, if not bemusedly, at the romance of the vine-ripened tomato and the predictable castigation of all things near and dear to the American heart. But their spins have little to do with slinging tuna *tartare* at a price point straddling maximum profit and the exact amount a customer is willing to pay.

Even if you do it right you can fail. The business is so much more than competitive wine lists, the right lighting, and oversized plates with odd-numbered dots of essenced oils. Genius cookery is hardly the silver bullet, nor is location, location, location. For the few that prevail, failure nips at the heels. So you work extremely hard reinventing the already invented, redefining exactly what fresh means on the plate and how you look at things. That bored me to aggravation. However, I relished having complete control over the occasional insufferable attention-hungry patron, one of the true delights of owning your own business. You simply don't have that working for someone else.

Jenny and I worked hard and we made money. We even managed to build a sustainable measure of wealth, which is mildly to wildly remarkable if you think about it. Don't we all know people who make tons of money and have nothing to show for it? I know individuals—in the restaurant biz particularly—who've spent hundreds of thousands of dollars to build shops they feel enslaved to. To sum up and average what they say about that: "I spent my life savings to buy a job that pays me less than someone else would." Ouch.

Where does all the money go? Jenny and I were too damned busy to waste all of what we made and too scared at the prospect of going the usual restaurant route of having pushy, cash-infusing partners. I think we'd rather have stayed up at night—we were up anyway. The days were long and the dishwashing crew was always on vacation.

As I write this I can't help feeling a bit childish, if not small, about what I've revealed so far. I just turned off a television program about custom-made sailboats with mahogany interiors, toys available to those in a much different financial bracket. I know people who've gotten really rich on Intel stock. Custom-made sailboats. Intel gazillionaires. Now that's a lot of money. Still, our kind of money for a couple with no kids is basically disposable and we spent it accordingly, especially on the trappings that promised us relief, reward, and prestige.

It was an achievement that I never took lightly. I grew up without much in a seaside village on Guam, an island as geographically remote as it is vaguely present in our popular awareness, in a world not at all the sandy beach, bamboo bar stool and OP beach wear. Kids my age spent our long Catholic school days thinking of someplace else and dreaming of being someone else, kind of like the person I became. We groveled at the feet of sailors' children, vying for vicarious encounters with snow, J. C. Penney, Knott's Berry Farm, and Twinkies.

At around noon in a rear dining room, I was dusting a newly completed wall in a building we had purchased and renovated, and into which we had moved the business from a previously leased location. We were ready to greet the impending Y2K more charged up about our destinies than we had ever been. I have to admit, though, that boldly greeting the new century was a notion that meant considerably less on 2/12 than just being able to tell the carpenters *Good-bye and take your damn nail guns with you*. At last, construction was completely over.

A few hours later we sat customers in that particular dining room for the first time. The dinner service proceeded as usual, and by eleven o'clock Jenny's was empty, except for diners at two tables in a front room on the other side of the building.

Tall palm trees had been delivered shortly after service started and were quickly shoved into a discreet corner. I was supervising their placement sitting down. It was the first time I had been able to really just sit down since the previous July when construction began. Cool. I was proud and happy. The daily drywall dust-chasing dance was over. My days of cheerleading the anxious staff, who were a little freaked out about moving, the what-ifs, and my inability to be kind, were officially over. The fronds of the palm trees softened the edges of our new concept and I took a deep breath on a gleaming new banquette and enjoyed the moment.

Jenny shared it with me.

"All right! I can die now!" I sighed, relieved and exhausted.

"How about we just go home and sleep," she said, equally spent.

I agreed.

She said she first needed to wash her hands and I said I would meet her in the front office. We rose from the banquette. She headed her way and I, mine, giving the newly finished dining room a long look up and down. I looked up at the ceiling fan, checking to see if it was balanced. It was. I turned around and walked toward the office.

On my way, I noticed without too much concern that I was still seeing the ceiling fan oscillating in the corner of my left eye. I blinked a couple of times at the curiosity. It was as though the pictures that eye was processing were double-exposed and actually moving. I saw the goings-on in the restaurant through the ghost image of the rotating ceiling fan.

I blinked several more times, thinking and hoping the fan would fade. It didn't.

Perturbed, I walked quickly into my office and sat down to wait it out but my moving picture was getting more intense. The fan had now become the stronger image while the rest faded to a blurry darkness. In an instant, all I could see in my left eye was a set of white oscillating blades against a black background. It then moved slowly across the other eye and stopped.

It stayed there and rotated, taunting me with a quiet resolved menace.

My heart pounded and I began to sweat. The numbing sound of a helicopter was suddenly all I could hear.

I stumbled out of my office and through the dining rooms, calling out for Jenny. I managed to push open the door to the ladies' room, where I hoped she would be.

"Call 911!" I cried.

Jenny grabbed me. She was confused by the commotion and understandably concerned for the two tables finishing their dinner. I convinced myself I was dying of an exploded brain. I shouted to the unseen staff to call 911. Jenny forced me back to the banquette where just three minutes before we had sat admiring the palm trees and congratulating ourselves. My breathing got short, my heart pounded to new levels, and I passed out.

I then had a major seizure.

While convulsing, I bit my tongue and blood ran down the side of my mouth. I can only imagine how this must have added to the spectacle. When people come out of seizures, quite often they are violent. I certainly was. Two large paramedics, two waiters, and three cooks wrestled me onto a gurney. One of the waiters later said they wondered if I had taken angel dust. He said he looked me in the eyes as I lunged at him and saw that they were black and vacuous.

I don't remember any of it. To hear it described now makes me uneasy because one of the things I immediately understood to be real at the moment I regained consciousness was that my pants were off. And wouldn't you know it? There was nothing between me and my Calvins. I struggled to put my hands over my privates or reach for my clothes, but handcuffs restraining me to the gurney prevented me from doing anything.

I kept repeating, "I'm sorry."

Later I thought, "Holy shit!"

So there I was, surrounded by a staff who received, I am sure, major payback for enduring years of my demanding perfectionism. Handcuffs on and weenie out. Well, mostly in. It was February in the Snow Belt.

I'd been somewhere outside my body.

For a split second before I was conscious of my situation, I experienced a luxuriously pale atmosphere and an astounding feeling of flight. I hovered somewhere over the parking lot outside, deaf and foggy. But then I heard a bloodcurdling scream. Someone was screaming at the top of his or her lungs. I flew to where the screaming emanated. The instant I arrived at the sound source I realized that it was me who was doing the screaming. I fell. The words I'm dying turned from an awful deafening sound in my ears to a painful, bloodied scream in my throat.

I was incoherent for thirty minutes. I awoke half-naked, mortified, terrified, confused, and feeling betrayed. My throat ached from the screaming. It was hot and felt like the melting skin of a ripe tomato plunged into boiling water so it could be easily peeled.

What followed were months of tests at Chicago's best hospitals, which could not reveal a single identifiable reason why I'd suffered a seizure, nor was there evidence of any neurological damage. Beyond the tests and the disappointment (yes, I was actually disappointed I couldn't get diagnosed with a *bona fide* ailment) was a profound—and I mean profound—depression. My sense of personal power crumbled while I whimpered and retreated. I became a hopeless hypochondriac, downloading every possible medical site on a really slow modem. I grew obsessed with death. Slowly, I overcame that depression to become obsessed with life. It became all too clear to me that life, indeed, is very short.

February 12, 1998, was a lifetime ago. I think it was my first real milestone, more personally significant than beating the odds set by my remote upbringing and eventually finding myself in a position where I was regularly serving Muhammad Ali Pecan-Encrusted Pork Chops on Sauteed Cabbage with Garlic Mashed Potatoes. It was, in medical terms, an inconsequential seizure, probably set off by my brain getting caught in a visual loop (the ceiling fan). An electrical storm inside my head.

In the days, weeks, and months that followed I tried desperately to take it easy by spending more time at home to relax and nurse my psyche within walls that were supposed to be a life-giving haven. It never happened. Because I was taking it easier, Jenny spent a few more hours at the restaurant and I found myself alone a lot facing the cold truth about what it took to be truly relaxed in our house. It wasn't a big secret. For me then, as now, it took the chores being done so I could just relax. Nothing New Age about that. But in that house? It had never occurred to me just how many chores there were in a house lifestyle gurus would be proud of.

There are chores, and then there are chores. The first set involves the usual cleaning, errands such as shopping for food, getting a quick oil change, perhaps going to the post office. The second set, the "styling" chores, are those that we've all heaped on our schedules in the pursuit of house beautiful. I hate this new set of chores—arranging endless pillows, refreshing windowsill vases, dusting wreaths, replacing votive candles, wiping bath and olive oil rings, refilling individual salt bowls. Individually these are simple tasks, but en masse and on a weekly (sometimes daily) basis, they are insidious.

I was finding out that Shabby Chic doesn't happen without crabby chic. When you really think about it, doesn't scrubbing the floor sound infinitely more worthy of your time than scraping beeswax candle drippings off every surface in your sanctuary?

Here's the crazy part: Jenny and I paid three people to help us keep house but I still found it unbearably difficult to maintain. They weren't live-ins, after all—who could afford that? But it wasn't as though we lived like the Victorians. On the contrary, we lived in a magazine cover with headlines that read "Casual Easy," "The Fabulous Great Room," "Why Kitchens Are the Center of Every Home," and "Provence in the Midwest Garden." But do you know how much work it takes to clean the trappings of that life "style"? Candles, glass, vases—all the shit you're supposed to buy, master, and maintain so you can live perfectly?

What a blow it was when I realized that cherished refreshment was not to be found in the very place it should have been. I thought we built it! All I wanted was a comfortable house that didn't have its maintenance schedule screaming at me. Guess what? I didn't have it. I heard myself repeating what my mother used to moan over and over: Get me back to work so I can relax!

I wasn't about to lose control for the second time, not in such short order at least. A mission, it seemed, had found me. I plunged myself into finding the nurturing paradise I had so effectively lost. What happened? What *happens*?

Peace of mind and happiness are way too much to ask of a house. I'm afraid that as havenlike as we think we can create them, they remain vacuous in spite of the accessories and architecture. You never really achieve your own home by copying what someone else's looks like. Sorry. M. F. K. Fisher and Peter Mayle have caused more strife due to emulation than pleasure with their writing, take it from *moi*. Felon or not, Martha Stewart has a staff, *The Staff*. It takes a tremendous effort by fiercely talented people to bring her to the calm, charming, and casually organized place you see on TV and in print. We've all imagined what the morning commute to Martha Stewart Living Omnimedia from the tristate area must look like from outer space. Can you see all these really good-smelling people speaking a craft-and-style language with precisely outfitted glove compartments—if they drive—or emergency sewing kits if they take public transportation? You and I don't have staffs.

Not that some of us can't afford them, but more about that a little later. For me, it's about loving my wife, my dogs, friends, and family in the purest way and, above all else, finding me amid the clutter.

The process by which I am achieving this small, lofty ideal has been technically simple: We downsized, literally. Yet on the everyday, imperfect, human level, it has sometimes been practically impossible because everybody thought we were either crazy or were going through some spectacular financial ruin. Our immediate public couldn't move from *Pommes Anna, Côtes du Rhône,* and big bouquets of delphinium and larkspur to an ambulance and a new attitude without misguided suspicion. That kind of scrutiny is difficult. Slowing down, after all, requires getting out of the proverbial fast lane. I am challenged daily fending off this feeling that I'm missing out on the magic in my previous life. Thankfully, I've learned to ask myself: What magic? Every time I make that inquiry I find that I am infinitely happier and much more fulfilled today than I ever was. Mercifully, I believe, so is Jen. I ask her all the time.

So here's my big secret: Simplifying and slowing down require a significant degree of sizing down.

It isn't, contrary to popular belief, that you buy a dilapidated eighteenth century farmhouse in upstate New York, restore it, telecommute, organically raise your crops, and spend endless weekends poking through the mold-hell of every country antique store in search of crap. How easy is fending off marauding deer from your leeks and cabbages in Bugville versus pushing your cart down the organic aisle at your local supermarket? Give me a break. Nor does the secret lie in the fabulous makeover that bestows tear-jerking style in just 48 hours for the low price of $1000. That, my friends, is crapola.

Simplifying today has more to do with choice than size. The American home is huge by comparison to how the rest of the world lives. The middle class has tricked itself into believing that bigger rooms and a cover garden make life better and easier, and that home ownership, period, is the supreme form of validation. But the truth is that a big house only guarantees a big mortgage and more chores. Consequently, our homes are first-aid kits cluttered with every kind of painkilling furniture and trance-inducing gadget, all marketed, designed, and purchased for the sole purpose of making us feel better about being absent from our lives and the pursuit of our dreams. Our homes have become residential convention spaces with great rooms, master suites, and lavatories that have turned going to the bathroom into a public spectacle. Do you really care that your bathroom is large enough to have an audience watch you go? Watch HGTV sometime. Practically every "dream bathroom" includes space for a fluffy chaise or overstuffed chair. Wouldn't you rather have a conversation over a cup of tea than while you're relieving yourself? Moreover, if you're going to spend money on seating, shouldn't most of it go where you're going to do most of the sitting?

If you've opened this book, it may be that you're feeling overwhelmed or at least curious. Come in, my pants are back on. Don't mind that I'm going to get preachy sometimes.

RESCUE VOCABULARY

STYLING CHORES
Chores related to objects in your home that serve little or no primary function except for contriving a mood.

EXAMPLE
Scraping candle wax off the bathtub rim; dusting silk grapevines that cascade over your drapes; replacing dead Siamese fighting fish that used to swim in your clear vase of lucky bamboo.

EXERCISE
Determine how many styling chores you have.

two

I lay in a bed being monitored for abnormal brain activity in St. Agony's, which is what the residents of Harbor Country call St. Anthony's Hospital. Harbor Country, a collection of lakefront resort towns in southwest Michigan, is about an hour's drive from downtown Chicago. Its towns, with names like New Buffalo, Union Pier, Lakeside, Harbert, and Sawyer, were established to harvest the hardwoods that rebuilt Chicago after its great 1871 fire. The flames must have been frightfully visible across Lake Michigan—even today, on clear, smogless days on the beach in New Buffalo you can make out the modern Windy City skyline.

Harbor Country and Chicago sandwich a tiny stretch of Northern Indiana that itself boasts beach enclaves like Grand Beach, Michigan City (St. Anthony's is here), Beverly Shores, Tremont, and Porter. The Indiana lakefront and dunes are unique and particularly beautiful, part of the protected Indiana Dunes National Lakeshore.

As one drives from Chicago east on Interstate 94 into Harbor Country, the fabled wrong and right side of the track become apparent. On the left side, the lake side of the track, are the aforementioned towns. On the right are miles of farmland dotted with small country towns that are typical of the Midwest stereotype. Outwardly and, especially in its own mind, Harbor Country is as different from that wholesome corn-fed image as the Lake Superior mill towns are from the Hamptons. In fact, an overly imaginative lifestyle writer or two have dubbed Harbor Country "Chicago's Hamptons." Fair enough, except in the Hamptons, there is actually money accompanied by authentic high society with its soft-spot for new ideas. We were simpler folk blessed with the occasional Oprah sighting, but cursed with a short-sighted dedication to house, garden, food, and personal makeovers. Though our sleepy lake towns lacked progressiveness, Dom Perignon, and cocker spaniels with personal assistants, they more than compensated with a comically annoying pretentiousness imported by an impatient, easily impressed, weekend clique of aging Chicago yuppies.

Jenny and I often said that opening our own restaurant in Harbor Country was practically the same as setting up shop on any trendy street in Chicago. The same faces showed up in Michigan who had come to the several restaurants where Jenny cooked when she was a partner with one of the city's prestigious restaurant groups. The edge Harbor Country gave us, apart from Jenny's separation from her partners and my only invitation to join an otherwise closed group, was the country—the lake, the stars, the acreage, the parking. One might think that chucking it all in 1992 was the innest thing to do, although it was quite controversial that Jenny left her very stable and high-profile positions, particularly for someone like me. I was all too aware that Jenny (in her early thirties) was at least supposed to marry someone of her own professional stature, perhaps a wine importer with personal verticals of Bordeaux. I was twenty-five, barely thirty months out of college, eager, though decidedly undecided. Jenny's critics and friends only knew me as a young guy of ethnically murky origin who delivered fish. That I attended college on a full academic scholarship and wanted to become a writer got lost. Jenny had just been named Chicago Woman Chef of the Year. Was she crazy hooking up with me? We did it, anyway. And I secretly took pride in scripting the most concise, no-bullshit menu in the Midwest.

While Jenny's talents and sustained media magnetism surefired our successes at Jenny's Restaurant, fulfilling every one of her professional goals, I found it very difficult. Indeed, it was nearly impossible to obtain a fair measure of credit for my contributions. I mean, cooking and the chef's prestige do not an entire eatery make. I did the rest.

I needed something to satisfy my emerging megalomania and awkward sense of style. A big new house on a couple of acres in Union Pier seemed just the thing. A tower, as it were, to which I whisked my worthy bride. It was easy. Harbor Country was filled with builders willing to give rapt attention to anyone (which was everyone) stabbing at a picture from a shelter rag anxiously clutched in the other hand. And when the structure was completed, antique shop after art gallery after Shabby Chic distributor after beeswax candle hawker after garden center lined the old roads to Detroit.

At St. Agony's, I shared a room with a hairy leg attached to an ugly foot with toenails that looked like crunchy triangles of Greek baklava. The rest of him was hidden behind grommets and flyaway poplin, hardly the stuff that makes good soundproofing. He screamed for hours that his back was killing him. Nurses came and went, responding to his electronic summons or to his considerable wailing, only to tell him that they had paged the doctor on duty and he would be by as soon as he could. Apparently, there were a lot of emergencies.

Compared to my roommate, I was lucky. I was only completely freaked out, planning my funeral, and rewriting "Candle in the Wind" as an elegiac hymn. At least, I wasn't in physical pain. And I was beginning to think I could actually get over having my dick and balls exposed to my entire staff.

Jenny visited me early the first morning and left quickly as she was gearing up for Valentine's Day. At around 11:30 pm she came back.

I had spent the day completely unhinged.

"Have you been crying?" she said, concerned though visibly tired.

"Yeah."

"The doctor says they can't find anything, so that's good, right?"

"Why did I have the seizure then?" I whined.

There was nothing good about having convulsed into unconsciousness for no reason. The reins with which I drove the mighty coach had been snapped.

"I can't believe this is happening," I moaned. "Who's watching the front of the house anyway?"

Jenny sat on the bed. "It's all right, honey," she said. She told me that our longtime hostess, Aimee, had been handling it.

"She's been dying to manage, you know that," said Jenny. Her patient frown turned up and she smiled.

"Yeah, well, I'm dying to manage," I said. "Shit, I'm just dying."

"No you're not, silly."

Jenny rolled her eyes patiently, the way she had done so many times as she had watched me quickly, though sometimes not so gracefully, mature into a confident and able restaurateur.

"Let's give Aimee that promotion, OK?" she said. "She knows everything you know. You've set it up. Now you can pass it on. I want you to rest."

The Leg had been getting a full-body CAT scan. After Jenny left, I saw that it was attached to a groaning man about my age who was now being wheeled to his corner. He smiled weakly at me and I smiled quickly back at him. It was clear he'd finally gotten some pain medication.

His wife pulled back his privacy curtain. "Woo-wee, you smell," she told him.

"Well, you'd be sweating yer tits off if you had a broken hip, woman!" he grunted.

"How the hell was I supposed ta stop you from convulsing if I didn't jump on yer ass!" she argued.

"Shit! You didn't have to break my hip, girl!" he replied almost cheerily.

"I practically broke the damn TV," she said through deep, smoky chuckles.

"Fucked up that I can't smoke here," he said. His layered phyllo toenails made me wish my own curtain was pulled around me. I rang the nurse.

"Yes?" a voice said. A thin woman with pork-rind hair came in shortly after I pushed the button.

"Do you know when I'll see the neurologist again?" I asked.

"You'll have to make an appointment with him after you check out tomorrow."

"You mean he won't see me again while I'm here?" I said, shocked. I couldn't believe it. I was in dire need of attention.

"Your tests are fine." That was her final, flat answer.

I urged her to pull my privacy curtain. She sniffed the air, looked at me, and realized that the fumes were coming from the leg. I couldn't smell it, thank God; my nose was stuffy from crying. But from the nurse's expression, I guessed it approximated Emmenthaler on a hot dashboard. I dozed off thinking about how a full-grown shattered hip could go unnoticed in a screaming, putrid man in, of all places, a hospital.

I couldn't wait to go home, to my fantastic house that had been outfitted for our every comfort.

I imagined a bath in the oversized Jacuzzi tub with foofy bath salts, bubble bath, and the eight-dollar herbal bath sachets from the bath shop in Lakeside. I'd step out onto the knobby cotton dreadlocks of the white bathmat from ABC Carpet and Home on Broadway in New York. I'd dry off with Ralph Lauren bath sheets from Michigan City, and throw on a cotton waffle-weave bathrobe from the Chambers sale catalogue. Then I'd smear French L'Occitane shaving cream on my sparse beard and splash on some kind of Jamaican Rum aftershave. I'd pull on woolly socks from Portugal and walk downstairs for large quantities of San Pellegrino sparkling water in glasses from Crate & Barrel or Sur La Table. Then I'd sit on one of the sofas in the great room to warm myself by the Rumford fireplace faced with handmade Indiana bricks. But not before I had lit a couple of aromatherapy candles and gathered the two dozen lifestyle catalogues that had arrived in the mail.

As I lay in Agony's, thoughts of these mundane luxuries and new disturbing ones about Greek food nearly kept me from recognizing that (despite my being freaked out) I was as physically comfortable as I had been in many years; significantly less distracted by my surroundings, in a shared room with a stinky guy so obviously not of Harbor Country ilk.

Jenny called me shortly after sunrise to ask how I was doing. She said that if I could bear to go on without her for just one day, she needed to meet an HVAC technician at the restaurant to correct the thermostat in our expensive new walk-in cooler. I told her I was fine and cursed the company that had installed it.

"I'll be by at five when you get released, OK?" she said.

"If I'm alive."

I ate a surprisingly good breakfast of oatmeal and yogurt, completely un-like the Bronx bagel platter with soft scrambled organic eggs I normally ate on Wednesday mornings at the breakfast place in Lakeside, where Jenny and I would window-shop for pillar candles in the boutique next door.

The neurologist who had ordered and interpreted the results of the CAT scan, MRI, and other tests came by finally. He was Czechoslovakian, and greeted me with a quick, impersonal attempt at *Hello, how are you feeling?*

I wanted to tell him that I was a little depressed and so forth, but before I could do that, he pulled a pen out of his pocket and ripped my sheets off. My gown was twisted above my waist. As I'd been on the floor of the restaurant thirty-six hours before, I wasn't wearing underwear.

"Maybe you should wear your panties," he remarked loudly. His face hinted at disgust.

I immediately became pissed off, if not self-conscious about my linger-ing pantless Winnie-the-Pooh moment. Oh, fuck him. So I asked him twice to repeat what he had just said, knowing it was difficult for him to enunciate clearly. He ran the tip of his pen across the sole of my foot.

"Ow!" I strained.

Then he did it to the other foot. He told me to call his office in South Bend to schedule a follow-up appointment in a couple of weeks. He gave me his card. When he left, I crushed it in my hand, threw it deliberately onto the floor and made a mental note: Get yourself to a real doctor in Chicago.

As I stepped into our house, I saw that Blanche and Marie, the cleaning ladies who came once a week and as needed, had been there. The fireplace was stacked with a tower of oak and birch with a waxy, fire-starting brick set out ready to light. Someone had sent a large saucer filled with mixed spring bulbs from one of the two town garden centers (I could recognize a tag). A gigantic still-fresh bouquet (the restaurant's previous week's delivery) was on the dining-room table in a great clear bowl. Even the dogs—Ada, the pointer, and Beatrice, the bloodhound—gleamed. They must have just come back from the dog herbalist/groomer.

Jenny lit the fire and walked me upstairs, where she ran me a bath. A quick peck and thirty seconds later she dashed downstairs to head for the restaurant.

"We're going to be slammed tonight," she said quickly. We always were on Valentine's Day.

The bath was never more necessary, but in the perfumed silence I sensed that the house was restless and temperamental. Outside, I could see frown lines at the eves where the ice had dammed. A bead of silicone caulk between the picture window and the bathtub seemed no longer willing to be taut and waterproof. It sagged. The pink marble vanity seemed to say to me, "Hurry up and feel better, will you, so you can buff me with the stuff you're supposed to slather on me once a year."

Behind me the shower hissed, "Maybe now you'll have the time to order that glass door."

A gardenia-scented candle begged to be lit. I reached over to grab it but it slipped and fell into the water, resurfacing upside down. The price tag read $24. Oh well, I thought, the fancy lighter needed fluid anyway.

I was beginning to get a sinus headache so I walked downstairs to the kitchen, and poured myself a glass of sparkling water and washed down a couple of aspirins. I walked to the sofa and breathed deeply. From where I sat, I could see that Blanche and Marie had missed an entire pane of glass on a kitchen cabinet that had been sprayed with Windex. A diaphanous slime swam between the flower stems on the dining table. A noise in my head beeped, sounding an alarm that had been off while I'd been away. A secret noise, it was my able assistant at the restaurant that rarely quieted. It was back.

"Damn," I said. "There's shit to do."

RESCUE POP QUIZ

TOOLS NEEDED
• Blank sheet of paper
• Pen or pencil

ON THE TOP OF THE SHEET
Write everything you know about preventing brain aneurysms.

TURN THE SHEET AROUND
Write driving directions to your local Home Depot, including shortcuts and times to avoid traffic.

THINGS TO ASK YOURSELF
Why do you know more about Home Depot than about how your body works?
What hazards in your home parade themselves as lifestyle accoutrements?

three

March and April.

The timing sucked.

It wasn't enough that the best neurologists in Chicago were six months out for new patients. I'd managed to develop what turned out to be the worst sinus infection in sinus history, a condition that, despite any kind of allopathic therapy, simply had to run its course. It was awful. I couldn't lift my head. My ears rang. I was blowing mucus the color of Jelly Bellies. My head hurt with pressure and pounding. Even other people's tragedies didn't help matters. Jenny offered that when she worked with Wolfgang Puck in the eighties, a golfball-size booger with teeth and hair was removed from behind a family friend's cheek. But did I care?

I connected my symptoms directly to the seizure. This was a sure sign— one that flashed over and over in my head—that the Indiana CAT scan and MRI were faulty, and that the delicate Czechoslovakian neurologist who shrank at the sight of my meat and potatoes didn't know shit from chicken paprikash.

I managed to get a couple of appointments with my internist at the University of Chicago, who prescribed two rounds of powerful antibiotics. When the inevitable sour stomach arrived, it became further proof that the suspected brain tumor had spread. My attempts to confirm over the Internet what I had self-diagnosed were made very difficult by a 28K modem and un-reliable middle-aged Harbor Country phone lines.

Aimee, our newly appointed dining-room manager who had quit her job as a successful travel agent to join us full-time, was reliably complimentary of the house as we reviewed restaurant business.

"Aimee, have you ever had a sinus infection?" I asked, completely ignoring the bank reconciliation she had brought.

"All the time," she answered, intent on the paperwork spread out before us.

"I mean a really, really bad sinus infection so that you blew lime green and your ears – "

"Felt like you'd been swimming at the bottom of the pool all day?" she said.

"Yeah. My head feels like that, too."

"It's a sinus infection all right."

That morning I had blown my nose and the room had begun to spin to a high-pitched buzzing. I was sure I was having another seizure.

"Oh, that happens to me sometimes when I'm driving," she said nonchalantly. "It's something to do with the pressure in your ears."

Driving? I told her that if the same thing happened to me behind the wheel I'd drive right into triage at Sloan-Kettering.

If I was going to talk about my failing health, Aimee was going to raise her eyes to the vaulted ceilings twenty feet above as a saving distraction. She hadn't been to the house before, although we had talked about it during construction and mused over the madness that followed perfecting Midwest living. She was as willing to stop talking about business matters as I was, so long as she could tour the house. I reluctantly put a lid on my neuroses and gave her a pained showing. At least I was thinking about something other than my health, and, let me tell you, this house gave me a shitload to think about.

We had built the house in 1993 during the height of the Great Room Era. Five years earlier, a thirty-eight-hundred-square-foot-home would have had at least four bedrooms, a den, a formal dining room, and kitchen with breakfast nook. Not this one—the Great Open Plan was dogma and we followed it religiously.

Centered on the southwest wall of the 23-x-34 great room with 20-foot ceilings, was a 5-x-5 foot Rumford firebox enclosed by a 10-x-10 foot mantel flanked by two Pella French doors with gigantic transoms. All of the sixty-four windows and exterior doors were Pella, the must-have brand. Smack in the middle of this great room before the massive hearth sat two silk-covered couches and a pair of mint-condition, very desirable 1920s French club chairs. They flanked a nineteenth-century Indiana wood sled that served as a clever coffee table. Behind one of the couches was an early nineteenth-century French refractory table bought in London on a rare trip away. All of these sat on an expensive and gigantic Oriental rug.

On the poolside of the great room, to the right of the fireplace, was the dining area that sat ten. The featured piece was an 8-x-4 foot, nineteenth-century Mennonite pine table from the Southwest, with mismatched antique chairs. On the left side of the fireplace sat a Welsh dresser base, circa 1725; a leather chair, and 7-foot tall abstract sculpture. Once, like a TV decorating goon, I described this corner as "the reading area" when all it was was a corner with a chair. More pricey rugs were scattered throughout.

Twenty-five feet opposite the fireplace began a simple utilitarian kitchen that measured 15-x-25 feet. Eighty percent of it was a "sitting area" with a couch and chair – its own living room essentially. The appliances, sink, and counter were built along a bank of windows looking out onto the pool. Above the work space the ceiling soared through the second floor so that from the master suite—through a balcony—Jenny and I could look down at the kitchen and out onto the pool. Our architect thought this appropriate for a cooking couple. A walk-in pantry, my office, a laundry room, a full bath, and large guest room composed the rest of the first floor, not including foyers and landings inside the front and back doors.

The entire second story was basically our master suite and Jenny's cookbook library. Even though the bathroom didn't boast twin sinks (which made no sense to us anyway), it did sport his and her decks. Mine looked over the pool, Jen's looked out to the dogwood collection.

Downstairs, on the other side of the laundry room, another wing was being built as a long-term guest suite with a fieldstone fireplace, bathroom, kitchenette, and cathedral ceiling. This wing measured roughly 800 square feet. It was originally designated for Jenny's ailing mother, who passed away while it was under construction. We added the fireplace reasoning that it would be our section of the house when we were so old that we couldn't walk up stairs.

Outside, a 25-x-15 foot screened porch wrapped itself around the house. The French doors flanking the fireplace opened onto it. We outfitted the porch with more couches and chairs-and-a-half, ferns, sisal rugs, candles, and a dining-room table that sat six. A deck wrapped around the custom 60-x-20 foot pool. At the deep end, the deck turned ninety degrees to a custom tiled grill unit with a sink and two gas burners, terminating at French doors to the new guest wing. From here you could step down into...the Zen Garden.

Ah, the Zen Garden. It was a terrace of small river rock that I raked regularly so that the pine needles wouldn't un-Zen the Zen.

Directly west of the Zen Garden the deck stepped down once more into a semicircular landing of larger river rock. There, one could behold a $2,400 *Cryptomeria japonica* (Japanese cedar) that brought the two elements together, as they say. In its magnificent shadow there was a rose garden with thirty-six varieties on raised flagstone beds enclosed by the quintessential custom-milled picket fence. Beyond the fence lay the northeastern quarter of the property—which itself was another garden—directly outside the front door.

Oakleaf hydrangea skirted ancient blue spruce that defined the perimeter of our two and a half acres. I had installed walks throughout, made of painfully salvaged Chicago pavers I had personally sprayed with ten gallons of spoiled buttermilk. Along them, early-blooming Frillitaria gave way to Jacob's ladders that died back to white phlox, Snow-in-the-Summer, and thyme. The latter cascaded into creeping yellow sedum.

An intimate cottage garden hid behind a stately golden arborvitae, suggesting a portico to the southern half of the property beyond, where...

I installed a peony garden because it was Jenny's favorite flower, and planted it with every variety of peony available overnight from Gilbert H. Wild & Son. It was enclosed by a 20-x-40-foot "ruin," posts as thick as telephone poles, and rustic fencing that hinted at the remains of Abraham Lincoln's log cabin (you know, being so close to Illinois). I commissioned a potting shed to match the house, and filled it with every imaginable yard and garden tool. The rest of the southern forty was planted with a collection of grasses in a parterre formation. A well-paid metalworker had forged steel arches for a clematis collection, spring- and autumn-blooming varieties.

What Eden would be complete without water featuresssssssss?

A successful pond churned with ornamental carp and water lilies in the shady garden close to the front door, reached by meandering flagstone paths planted on either side with ferns and hostas that covered the thousands of daffodils that made the path yellow every spring. Back by the peonies, a not-so-successful round, brick-edged riparian expression heaved in its dryness. You see, it was placed in full sun and was too shallow, so it failed. Anyway, I planned to fill it with gravel and loam for a Siberian iris garden, so there.

Of course we had a two-car garage filled with a car we didn't use and inherited things from Jenny's mother, grandmother, and father, who had passed away in quick succession. Things like a five-hundred-pound butcher block, tables, more chairs and more garden furniture. What the garage couldn't hold was kept in the basement, itself already filled with camping gear and tools, old clothes, and more perfectly fine chairs.

Oh, yes. What wouldn't fit in the restaurant was squeezed into this house of ours. This included eight seven-foot Christmas trees that I'd packed away less than a month before I'd convulsed à la Harvey Keitel on the floor of the restaurant.

A month had passed since my seizure. The gardens were asleep, the pool covered, its iron-and-glass furniture packed into the cabana I forgot to mention was opposite the Japanese cedar. As it turned to April, I found that I was dreading the house to come as much as Aimee was dreading placating me by answering my questions about earaches, boogers, and stomachaches every time she came over to review the daily figures. What with the upcoming summer season at Jenny's and the house and all its charms, I was freaking out.

I bought a faster computer and was able to download new medical sites with detailed drawings instead of the text-only versions. I began studying the color of my stool, asking Jenny exactly what "clay-colored" looked like, while scrutinizing every clay object we owned. I descended into a hopeless, hypochondriacal depression.

Ascending from the cold earth were aconites and crocuses, little voices that in a few months would scream, "Deadhead me!" "Overplant me!" "Complement me with other varieties!"

The house cleared its own throat and choruses of pretty objects and accessories harmonized, readying themselves for the unnerving opera of spring.

RESCUE VISUALIZATION

VISUALIZE
The time before you knew what a "master suite" was, before "dream kitchens" were all the rage.

WERE YOU
Thinner?
Younger?
Healthier?
More financially flush?
Less cynical?

four

Wes and Bill ruled Harbor Country, as homosexuals so ably do in small aroma-therapied, slip-covered nations. When they didn't, they feasted their way to Atkins slim on *pollo* and *carne asada* at their villa in Mismaloya, Mexico, enjoying the kind of domestic service that Sharon Osbourne does. Jenny dragged me to their hacienda as my depression erupted into full-blown misery by May.

Wes and Bill did things like design display, giftware, and tables, all of which ended up on the cover of Smith & Hawken or on the set of the latest Julia Roberts movie. They flamboyantly entertained interesting sorts who designed the interiors of private jets and cursed that it was taking far too long for the Prada store to open in Chicago. They exchanged bargain buying tips, like it's cheaper to fly to Paris and buy Gucci than it is to buy in New York or Beverly Hills. The last time I could fit into Gucci I was in the sixth grade on Guam. Who knew people like them? Harbor Country would sooner jump off the Sears Tower than waste money on Gucci or Prada. I mean, think of all we could get at the Pottery Barn Factory Store.

Wes, Bill, and company were magicians. They knew how to conjure travertine gold from Formica dross. They harnessed the secrets of light itself. Task lighting. Ambient lighting. Up lighting. Halogen. They were really good at container planting; they could make it look like something in a magazine. Whenever the restaurant's florist suggested something new, I checked with Wes and Bill first. As I think about it, they even had a dog that looked like Vern Yip.

Wes and Bill referred lots of people to Jenny's. Truly, they helped make Jenny's the place to be. Most of all, they genuinely liked Jen and me and didn't treat us like trophy friends who could get them wine and foie gras at wholesale. We were instant pals; we constantly showered each other with at-cost goods.

I was miserable in Mexico. The domestic help practically spoon-fed us, and the ocean was in our faces. I tried—I practiced my Spanish with the cook while Wes and Bill disappeared in the mornings to pursue chiseled abs. Jenny was curious about the funny kind of Bisquick the cook used. The houseman spent the mornings restaining the beams and doors and whitewashing where mold or dust had attached to the stucco. In the afternoons he'd garden, wash out the dove cages, and clean the pool. I talked with him about how he would trim the poolside ficus trees into umbrella shapes when they matured. I wondered at the domestic magic, wishing for it in Michigan where the chores nagged me, even from afar. Inevitably, I'd think about it too much and steal away to look across the Pacific and despair.

"Sweetheart, I wish you could tell me what's wrong," Jenny said, in quiet exasperation.

She was at the pool when I returned to our room to sulk. Moments before, I watched as she walked calmly to me so as not to alarm the others.

"Honest, when I was walking in the village today I thought I was going to throw up. I would have eaten lunch and been a sport, but I couldn't," I said. "Do you think I have one of those deadly parasites?"

Wes had taken us to lunch on the beach that day. I was anxious, I wasn't any fun. He asked me impatiently what was wrong with me. I had no answer so I grew quiet and ruined the afternoon.

"Wes knows," Jenny said.

"I think I'm dying, Jen," I wept.

"You're not," she replied.

The week before I'd gotten another MRI and full checkup, including an upper GI and one of those stress tests where they inject you with dye and you run quickly between a treadmill and an X-ray bed. These were performed by a team from Northwestern Memorial Hospital. I had exhausted the University of Chicago team. I had brought a pulse monitor on the trip that almost didn't make it through customs. According to it, I was fine.

"So you don't want to have dinner with the House and Garden?" Jenny asked gingerly.

"Fuck no," I replied firmly. I couldn't stand them.

"See? You are OK," she said, smiling.

House and Jenny had been introduced by a mutual friend many years before I came along. House met Garden about the same time Jenny and I met, so we always had a special connection that way (at least according to House and only when Jenny was listening). House was a reasonably successful publicist, widowed by a husband who committed suicide on her 40th birthday. Garden could, himself, drive anyone to a self-inflicted demise. Together, they were the Stuzchkins.

Not only were H&G house possessed, they were also rabid collectors of crap. Their weekend cottage was filled with every kind of old glass door knob and duck decoy knock-off ever conceived and imported to Harbor Country (which was considerable). Garden's hobby was making pinecone baskets that could double as end tables. They were everywhere.

Every now and then, House invited us over for Garden's cooking, which was basically all things hollandaise, béarnaise, andouille-stuffed, or maple-syruped. Jen and I weren't food snobs, as people in our industry tend to be, but we easily agreed that his cooking was way too studied. We would have enjoyed cold fried chicken and lime Jell-O in good casual company. House would spend the entire night rearranging table top accessories, reminding us regularly to compliment Garden for his culinary masterpieces. Between them they were always shaking to death the latest martini recipe, stuffing olives, and styling their tabletop, which left plenty of time for me to mouth to Jenny *Can we go now?*

House once called me a star-fucker to my face.

For a long time, whenever Jenny wasn't in the room or wasn't paying attention, House would drop the Jenny-I-love-Dan act. But I was nice—occasionally I indulged her with a caviar connection I had kept from my fish-delivering days. For that she maintained civilities, if only to keep the roe coming. This cheap paddlefish roe—Chatannoga sevruga—wasn't anything to whore oneself over. I didn't tell her that. It was fun to watch her completely unmake herself for low-end fish jizz.

House and Garden vacationed in Mismaloya every spring. Just my luck.

Wes and Bill had their cook prepare a simple whole snapper Veracruzana. House couldn't stop asking how much the furniture cost, Garden turned his nose up at the food, and every now and then they'd give me an *Oh, hi, star-fucker* look. It ended early. They staggered home and we made fun of them. I had a rare laugh.

But no sooner had Jenny fallen asleep than my anxieties returned. Through the mosquito netting I saw to my horror that the ceiling fan was on. My heart pounded as I struggled from the folds to turn it off. In bed, I looked at it in pissed-off telepathic silence, warning it not to move.

When we left Mexico, Wes decided he couldn't accompany Bill to the airport with us because he had work to do with the help, although I'm sure it was owed partly to my tiring neuroses. We hugged good-bye and were soon on our way to Michigan. As the plane approached O'Hare Airport, I looked at Jenny.

"What kind of work do you suppose Wes needed to do with the help?" I asked.

"Bill said he was going to help the gardeners plant bamboo in the ravine. It's a shitty job so he wanted to help," she said.

Domestic help. Shitty job. Help the help.

"That's fucked up," I said. "Think of the legions of bacteria in that freaking ravine."

The plane had a turbulent landing. I added air travel to a growing list of random obsessions.

May was hard. The list was getting enormous.

RESCUE REALITY CHECK

The price of the average gourmet kitchen : **$ 85,000**

The average income for gourmet kitchen households: **$150,000**

The average number of hours these gourmands work weekly: **65**

The average number of gourmet meals cooked in same kitchen: **1.5**

Price differential of 1.5 weekly meals at Le Bernardin over 30 years: **$ 78,000**

The value of said $85,000 kitchen 30 years later: **$5,000**

The value of $85,000 in a passbook savings account with a shitty rate 30 years later, depositing a nickel for every time the kitchen didn't live up to the dream: **$185,000**

five

By June 1998, Jen and I resumed couples counseling.

(For all practical purposes they were oyster shit.)

For her birthday in 1994, I had given Jenny a lusty pair of black South Sea pearl earrings. We had been in Harbor Country for only two seasons. The house was growing larger than planned. She opened up the earrings and promptly told me they were too expensive. It crushed me.

The restaurant lay right on the Midwest Snow Belt, and that winter had been especially snowy. The expressways from Chicago were closed New Year's Eve weekend and Valentine's Day weekend, effectively cutting off about seventy-five thousand dollars of profit. Sure, it was a hairy time, but I didn't care. For one thing, I didn't know any better. I was also neck-deep in the starved-for-professional-validation pool. Anyway, by the time her birthday rolled around in June we had caught up, but we were in such disagreement over the earrings for several weeks that we sought professional mediation.

She said I was immature for buying the earrings.

I was shocked.

"Since when do you get to edit what I spend?" I boomed awkwardly.

I was incredulous, hurt, and embarrassed.

Our therapist was David Rose, who I believe was *the* psychiatrist to the who's who of Chicagoland's foodies. I'd always felt that David never had any patience for my youth and inexperience in what he considered my very prestigious grown-up world. As a therapist for a basically solid couple, David never, in my opinion, quite approached appropriate neutrality; however, as a diner at large, he was clearly easily impressed and enthralled. To him, Jenny was one of those magicians who made bouillabaisse, certainly one of his more illustrious clients. He always started our sessions reminiscing about some dinner he had eaten at a restaurant where she was a chef.

"Dan, don't talk to her like that," David said officiously.

I looked at him angrily and then glared at Jenny.

"Don't dismiss me," he said.

I stared at him squarely.

"Do you know how difficult you are to talk with?" he said. He wasn't interested in being a little bit on my side. It was, therefore, easy for me to argue my case.

"I work hard, too," I said firmly. "Half of the bottom line is mine. I get to spend some of it, don't I?"

I growled at David as though I glimpsed the future, fast-forwarding four years to my postseizure counseling and a Depakote prescription that was accompanied by a really dreadful side effect.

"Fuck you," I said menacingly. "I am not about to let the weather run my life. If I want to buy Jenny earrings, I'm going to buy her the damn earrings."

Jenny started to cry, then smiled sheepishly and became apologetic. I worried about her.

"Jenny," I said. "Now why on earth are you crying? They're only stupid earrings."

"She's upset because you were being overbearing," David said forcefully.

"Will you shut up!" I yelled. "She's crying because business is stressful sometimes."

Now Jenny was really crying. I was alarmed. Suddenly I didn't care about the dramatic nonsense taking place between David and me. Jen's breakdown immediately filled me with guilt. Was I overbearing? My God! Should we have stayed in Chicago? Wasn't this therapy? Weren't we supposed to scream?

"They're just too expensive," Jenny said quietly. "You weren't being responsible."

"Finances matter to her," David said.

That tone of his. I stopped myself from reaching for Jen's hand as I looked at them. Together they looked so correct.

"Jen?" I started quietly. "The damn exhaust fan cost forty-five thousand dollars. The walk-in refrigerator cost thirty-five thousand dollars. You never think twice about how much we spend for equipment at the restaurant. We don't even own the damn building!"

In 1994 we didn't. We leased our space like ninety percent of restaurants. My voice had gotten considerably louder.

"You need the exhaust fan and walk-in, Dan," David said flatly.

"We do," Jenny said.

"Give me a fucking break!" I snapped. I argued loudly that we didn't need to buy new, we could have bought perfectly fine used equipment. "But did I stand in your way? Now I give you earrings and you have the nerve to even think I should know better?"

"Maybe we should talk about medication, Dan," David said. "Are your mood swings always this off the charts?"

I quieted into a speechless sulk. Of course my mood swings were off the charts. We were in the fucking restaurant business! Some fuckhead from Chicago could turn a perfectly good night sour if he waited five minutes for a table or his bread basket wasn't full, even at dessert with his belt undone. No one in this business was sane.

"You know I'm a simple girl," Jenny said. "You know that. The day-to-day business is hard enough. I don't ever want to feel like we did this past winter. I don't want to have to worry about people not coming in the door. Where would I wear the pearls anyway?"

Jenny's matter-of-fact response seemed dangerously on target. I felt as though she had unleashed exactly the resentment I'd heard from others and feared most from her.

"You can wear them shoveling the fucking snow," I said. "Fuck you, David. You have shitty teeth." And I left.

Jenny got into the car a half hour later. We drove home and said nothing for a day. She broke the silence the next afternoon by telling me to take her out for a moderately priced dinner somewhere nice, so she could wear the earrings and so she could apologize.

Over dinner we laughed about the time House had offered to buy into the business if we gave Garden a sous chef position. The thought of it! We renewed our commitment to each other and Harbor Country and exorcised some insecurities. We survived the pearls.

Our business doubled. Jenny became more comfortable with what became my habit of getting her a nice pair of earrings every year for her birthday. In exchange, I'd have to at least tolerate David Rose on a semi-regular basis.

Now I was seeing him one-on-one to talk about why I'd been so freaked out since my seizure. Mexico had failed. It was time to bring in the Jewish therapist.

I admitted I was becoming afraid of the restaurant. I told him I felt that it was sucking the life out of me and that my seizure was a sign it would one day kill me. Once I ran out of the kitchen when I stood too close to the exhaust fan and heard the deep whoosh of the fans. Another time, I cried for three days in a row because I was terrified of dying young, an episode that had started innocently enough while cleaning whole John Dories at home and finding one dead baby fish after another as I gutted them.

David declared the obvious—I was depressed—and suggested a couple of medications. I resisted, arguing that I was only taking longer than usual getting over a scary first-time health crisis. I didn't need pills, I needed time. I didn't want medication.

Then one day he suggested that I was bipolar. And it scared the shit out of me.

"I've just been through the scariest time of my life. Why wouldn't I be freaked out?" I argued as if for my life.

"What do you mean your house is talking to you?" he asked.

"I don't mean it's talking to me, talking to me. I meant it's a demanding house and wherever I turn, there's something else to do," I said.

"Most people don't hear crocuses sing – "

"Obviously they aren't singing Mariah fucking Carey. I'm not the only one who's heard the symphony of the forest. I'm just saying that it's a high-maintenance house, David. It screams at me, PRIMP ME, FUSS OVER ME, DO ME. That's all."

Boy, was that a mistake to say. Obviousy David's house was all discount European leather and Berber carpeting in some cerebellum ghetto high-rise.

The following week during a couples session, contrary to an agreement I had with him, he brought up medication for my supposed bipolar disorder. And for the second time since we had been seeing him, I walked out before our time was up.

I waited for Jen in the car. Saying nothing, she opened the passenger door and slipped between the rungs on the dashboard vent a prescription David had written. We drove home silently.

The next day I contemplated a last-ditch effort: going to the Mayo Clinic. I thought of packing my bags and leaving Jen a note that I was going to real neurologists and experts, not the half-dozen Chicago hacks I'd wasted my time with. But, instead, I drove to the pharmacy and had the prescription for Depakote filled. I took it as directed.

July 27th.

After I had failed to remain erect for the third time, Jenny and I lay side by side.

"Goddamn it, I hate that fucking restaurant," I muttered, really meaning the Depakote, quietly enduring flashbacks of my dick on display in subzero February.

"I hate that you hate it," Jenny said.

I quickly suggested that we sell the restaurant, reasoning that we could more than pay off the mortgage, put a chunk of change in the bank, and spend our time keeping house. We could garden and write cookbooks. We could probably even collect rent on the building if someone just bought the business.

"I thought about that yesterday actually," Jenny said.

"You did?" I said, surprised.

"But I'm not staying in this town if we sell the business," she replied in an alarmingly matter-of-fact tone.

"What?" I sat up. "What about our house?"

"What about it? If I want to bake cookies at the bakery in Union Pier, I don't want to endure the slander. You know how this town talks."

"Just tell them the truth."

"Which is?"

"I don't know," I replied. "Just that we were sick of it."

"Then they'll ask why we were sick of it," she said. "Plus I'm not sick of cooking."

"Not true, you know you get aggravated all the time," I argued. "And when you step away, you know the food isn't the same. It doesn't matter that we have sous chefs."

"Still, I'm not sick of cooking."

"They don't need to know that. Just say we were sick of it all," I said.

"But there's nothing to be sick of. We're doing great!" she said. She was right. We were.

"If we sell the restaurant," she announced calmly, "I'm not staying in Harbor Country. It's that simple."

I rolled on my side in passive disbelief. Jenny rolled to hers and pressed her butt into the small of my back.

"What are you thinking?" she whispered as I panicked in silence.

RESCUE MEDICATION

OTHER PROBABLE CAUSES OF MALE IMPOTENCE

Peeling paint.

Bad tulip color combination.

Not pronouncing Italian food words correctly.

Depakote, and other drugs that require a regular liver scan so your passions are diminished in a non-life threatening way.

Star-fucking Jewish therapists.

The restaurant business.

Innuendo in a precious lakefront community.

six

Jenny had gone mad.

Sell the restaurant—her restaurant? With her name alone on the aw-
ning? Her name on a Michigan liquor license that itself was as valuable as the
real estate? On a title for a building she owned? These were things few chefs
in Chicago could boast. Everyone in the business knew at least one person
who had some kind of payment plan with the IRS – but no one was that
lucky with his landlord. This was a business that made landlords rich first.

I was only thinking that the grass needed to be cut, the pool needed to be
medicated, and the roses needed to be rid of Japanese beetles. Maybe I'd try
Milky Spore since last year's six-hundred dollars' worth of beneficial nema-
todes were jacking off in someone else's yard. Then the mulch needed to be
refreshed, the recycling needed a discreet place to hide, and the hanging pots
needed replacement.

It was now August. I was thinking that friends were about to be coming over a lot to grill on the custom unit next to the pool. This meant that
I had better get some kind of refrigeration out there because it was way too
inconvenient to be marching in and out of the house for something cold. I
thought about coolers and frowned because that meant I'd have to go to the
store a lot for bags of ice. I thought of the mosquitoes and citronella candles
in metal buckets that you couldn't keep out because rainwater collected in
them. I thought about our iron-and-glass pool furniture and remembered
that Wes and Bill had theirs coated with polyurethane once a year. I wondered if the high-school kid who took away the grass clippings and weeded

would be reliable this year. I wondered how come the jets in the Jacuzzi scraped my knuckles so badly when I wiped off the coagulated bath oil after Jenny's bath.

That's all I was thinking. I only mentioned hating the restaurant at a (pardon me) vulnerable moment. Really I was just suggesting that we slow down and have a life.

Alas, the truth was surfacing. Since it had been built, the only time we interacted with the house was to service it, literally, to explain it by conducting silly tours to guests who thought they were being nice by asking to see it. To others, it seemed like we were living some kind of magazine-cover life. Well, we weren't.

On the inside it was like being, as the English say, downstairs. The house itself was decidedly upstairs. It was the pampered one. Owning that house was a job physically harder than feeding eight hundred people a week, harder even than doing the week's dishes at Jenny's. Not just eight hundred dishes—multiply eight hundred by bread plate, butter dish, salad plate, appetizer plate, entrée plate, dessert plate, coffee cup, and saucer. More like six thousand four hundred dishes. That was easier—I mean it—I'd spent many years doing just that. "Restaurant owner" is just a fancy name for "on-call dishwasher."

Still. What the hell was Jenny thinking?

She essentially scared me out of my depression. Nothing was more depressing than the thought of being accused of yanking her away from a good thing a second time. No thanks, or, as the waiters used to say, reviewing their tips for the night, Fuck you very much. I promptly returned to work and ran Jenny's with the eagerness of a Mormon on a bike mission.

"What would you say if we changed the house?" I asked Jenny one day.

I was reconciling the bank account just as I'd always done, save for those few months during which I lived the lyrics of "A Whiter Shade of Pale." It was a few days after Labor Day. The summer season was over and business had normalized from crazy to bustling.

At her desk, Jenny studied the latest wine catalogues. "What do you mean, 'change'?" she said, putting them down.

"I don't mean let's spend money to change," I said. "I mean I want to simplify. I'm back at work, obviously, and I'm healthy again and I just can't stop thinking about all the work that needs to be done at home."

"You mean a make-over?" she said.

"No, I mean the rituals that surround the stuff," I said. "The candles, the Windex, the making sure everything is in place and shiny so it looks the way it's supposed to look." I was trying so hard to explain that I completely flopped.

"Dan?" Jenny said tentatively.

I don't know if she was equally confused or if she was encouraging me to get my thoughts out. I know that somewhere in her head she was saying, You're the one with the big house butt-plug, you big dummy.

"That house isn't us, it just belongs to us," I said.

"It's screaming?" she said. Her mouth curled at the corner.

"Oh, you're funny," I warned.

"I like it, but it isn't me either," she said.

"We – I - built it for House and Garden, didn't I?" I said sheepishly.

"No, you built it for me. You were only thinking of me," she said.

Arrrgh.

"Go ahead. I trust you," she said.

And so began the rescue.

I recall the first meeting with the architect. Jenny's wish list included one thing: a bathtub. Mine was not so brief and was accompanied by layers of obnoxious ideas and cutouts from magazines and books. It was busier than Steven Cojocaru on the red carpet.

"We work so hard," I said. "When we come home, I want to feel like I can see where our money and effort are going."

Architects love to hear that. In the end, I think our architect succeeded. However, I didn't know then that the dream in blue toner on his drafting table would consume something more precious than money.

Time.

I took a hard look at the house. And then I grabbed a pad and pencil. The first signs of autumn were apparent - a chill weighed. The furnace was off for a couple of days while we waited for special filters for the geothermal climate-control system. (Never fool yourself that anything special has parts that are easily replaced.) I wanted to make a fire so I walked out behind the potting shed to retrieve some wood, after spending several minutes digging out the L.L. Bean log lugger from the cabana. Once inside the house, I set the logs on the hearth, rummaged for some waxy starter brick, and lit the fire.

The house immediately filled with smoke.

I had forgotten to open the flue. When I reached for the handle to turn it, a petrified mallard dropped onto the logs.

Ada and Beatrice leaped from their beds. The bloodhound bayed for what seemed ninety seconds before she hyperventilated. Ada was so excited she tried to flush more ducks out of the fireplace.

Shit, shit, shit.

I sat in front of the roaring fire. Twenty-five minutes had passed setting up this lovely scene. I felt guilty for a minute or two about using a large zip-lock freezer bag for the mallard carcass. This was silliness, I know - we only had full boxes of every size so that the plastic-bag drawer filled out nicely. Plastic bags we never used.

I titled three columns. Like. Hate. Missing. Under "Like" I wrote "bathtub." Under "Hate" I wrote a question mark. Under "Missing" I wrote "contentment."

Was I crazy? We were pigs in shit, and here I was complaining. I crumpled the page and threw it into the fire. Then I titled another page.

"Who am I?" I wrote.

Who are you?

RESCUE EXERCISE

WHO AM I?

(minimum 600 words)

TOOLS NEEDED

Blank paper

Pencil or pen

THINGS TO ASK YOURSELF

Am I a mother?

Am I a father?

Whose soulmate am I? What the hell does that mean anyway?

Am I spiritual?

What is my legacy?

TIP

Turn off Dr. Phil.

seven

Who I was wasn't the issue, really.

The big question was, "What the fuck have I done to my house?"

It was like a face with too much plastic surgery. Oh sure, I could understand a little boob lift—maybe that's what I needed, a house that suited our needs with a little bit extra. But this house was the New York Cat Lady socialite, the woman with the herd of little dogs on Chanel leashes, with a face that looked like she was being pulled down tight, clear plastic tubing feet-first.

It looked like a mouthful of new porcelain veneer teeth. The room were the Bachelor conducts his ridiculous rose ceremony. It was aww-shucks yellow labs spilling out of a gently-battered Volvo station wagon festooned with private beach stickers. It was by magazine and television standards perfect. It made me want to puke.

We did everything House Beautiful did, bought everything the catalogues sold, cultivated all Taunton published—all while working sixteen hour days. We were still tired on our days off. I thought long and hard about exactly how I spent my so-called downtime.

I tended to the garden if I wasn't sleeping. Don't get me wrong, there were parts of it that Jenny and I adored, but just parts. The only sections that I truly enjoyed were a small yard in the northwest quarter and the rose garden. The rest was unrelenting drudgery without any trace of innovation. We were merely collecting. To maintain a market value that reflected the actual cost of the house, the landscaping had to be equally obnoxious. In other words, real estate appraisers look for this shit. (The panic notion of "resale value" can really fuck things up.)

In the spring I slaved, in the summer I toiled, in the fall I raked those leaves for weeks when my garden helpers had the gall to return to their junior year of high school. Even during the winter I worried that the goddamned Japanese maples and broadleaf evergreens would freeze. Madness. I was always cleaning, sweeping, strapping on my electric leaf blower so it all looked tended, perhaps hopeful that by some benevolent combination of the right attachment and shadow-making light, one of my employees would catch a fleeting silhouette of me in the peony garden manhandling my really big cock.

We installed an expensive self-cleaning system in the swimming pool that was supposed to relieve us of traditional pool sweeping. Bullshit. I was fishing out more frogs than my ancestors ever fished from their wells. You can't stop God's critters from jumping! The outdoor gas grill? I'd like to strangle that retail Nazi from the Grill d'Toscano store at the mall.

I fled to work to take it easy. I did the math: We could have paid for years of live-in help and not lifted a single finger for considerably less than what we shelled out for that joyous abode filled with potential entertaining opportunities. I should have spent the thirty thousand dollars for the bathroom on a gold toilet seat. It would have been easier to clean and I could have taken it anywhere. Who were we? We weren't this!

I didn't want a bigger deck, I wanted a bigger dick! I jumped up and flushed the Depakote—those little orange emasculators—down the toilet.

And so who are you? Grab some Kleenex.

That floor? That kitchen? That wallpaper? They aren't you. Forget about it. They are choices you made at a certain time and place. You are an entirely different person now than you were when you chose that pickled pine plank. People are capable of changing and we often do.

On my weekly trips to the lumberyard, I'd pass their kitchen design area. Front and center was displayed a cabinet style that sported glass-front drawers for bean and grain storage. Sells like crazy, the salesman told me. I imagined the choruses of "Oh, that is so me. . . . "

Now think for a minute. How often are you really going to make cassoulet? No one I know wants to even think about butchering a duck at home, much less storing the confit and dealing with the gallon of fat splattered in the oven. I'm married to a chef. The polar ice cap is melting. The red lentils and star anise are maintaining their levels. Steadfast and leadlike.

I know what you're thinking. I've worked hard for my money, and damn it, I deserve my glass-front drawers! Well, yes, you do work hard for your money. The glass-front drawers are novel, but wouldn't you rather go out for cassoulet than be reminded constantly that you have NO TIME to soak the beans?

People are misled into believing that filling their homes with the latest and greatest will make their lives more comfortable and easy. We get caught up in the habit of displaying our wealth but we displace it instead. Yup, we end up using our hard-earned money to make our lives more difficult.

Wall after wall of top-of-the-line cabinetry? Fuck that. Endless feet of Italian stone surfaces, clear container after clear container of pasta and spice—every platter Williams-Sonoma has ever featured on its catalogue cover will not EVER make the task of preparing a meal easier than doing without. This is the honest truth: The only things that make cooking easier are (1) a sharp knife, (2) your favorite trusty pot, and (3) gas over electric. That's it, unless you hire a cook, which is actually a more prudent way to spend your money if you're looking to enjoy life. Dream kitchen my ass—get a goddamned personal chef.

A sharp knife, a good pot, a sturdy flame. All the rest of the stuff is Bengay for the overwhelmed. Dermablend for lifestyles blemished with stress. Take a look at your kitchen again. Open your cabinets, stare at the repeated themes, and try saying to yourself, "It's so me." I hope to God you have an epiphany—that kitchen is definitely not you. More, perhaps, it represents what you are not.

Who, then, are you?

There's no secret to finding the "you" within your home. Here you are:

YOU

You are you—your cells, your history, your memory, and your dreams. You are not a neutral palette. You are not a china pattern. You're not supposed to blend with the cupboards and carpet. You clash with yourself and others, and you don't match everything. You are an individual. You're definitely NOT what some queen on cable television tells you you'll become when you buy a hot glue gun.

But go ahead and write your definition down. Just don't make it some bullshit, crapped-up journal entry that's supposed to trim spiritual inches off your third chakra. (You thought you could rescue yourself with that six-hundred word number from last chapter? Hah!) State where you came from, where you are now, and where you want to go.

> I was born on June 17, 1967, on Guam. I married a great woman who'd love me even if I didn't try so hard giving her stuff she doesn't really care for. I worry too much about what people say about me, and strangely enough, I believe I'll stop that once I achieve a home where I can rest, so that I can focus on what I really want to do (which is write).

There you have it. It isn't Oprah's Book Club, hardly Pulitzer prize material, but it is, I feel, essentially who I am. Put your definition on paper and use a pen—not a computer, if you can at all help it. Handwriting your thoughts is an amazing exercise that causes you to choose your words and form your thoughts in a careful, deliberate manner. Your life is not going to be art you frame with seashells and copper tape that you'll give away at Easter with an attention-starved bottle of homemade bath salts.

Instead of spending another minute fussing over my house, I turned that energy inward, where, for the first time in a long time, I allowed myself to think like a writer, the person inside who was dying amid this lifestyle perfection. The script was my definition, and the set, what my house ought to have looked like. I know that you're thinking this is over the top. So what? So's your vinegar collection.

Here is how I fleshed out my production:

SOUND TRACK: I heard the music to the Italian film Cinema Paradiso, because I identified with the little boy who grew up in a small village and moved away. I heard Cole Porter and Sarah Vaughan and Saturday Night Fever. I know, I know. But it was my movie. You can make yours anything you want.

LIGHTING: Dark and dramatic. Lots of shadows but zero emphasis on the light fixtures themselves. None of this kind of lighting with tight wire and steel. No recessed lighting. Absolutely no halogen gadgetry. No recessed - no halogen? Now you really think I'm crazy.

SET DESIGN: New Orleans meets Manhattan apartment. No white walls or neutral-colored furniture. Not the house you'd find in Harbor Country. Victorian correctness without the fussiness. But fussy nonetheless in terms of the specificity of choice. The trim molding will be difficult if not impossible to get. This set feels like Two Fat Ladies meets The Talented Mr. Ripley.

Do not close this book.

Go with it. You did get suckered once into a Southwestern Santa Fe theme, for Chrissake.

Imagine how your movie will play out. I knew that my movie was definitely not prime-time TV, but that was perfectly fine with me. I wanted a place that you could only see at a fine arts theater. My life, after all, isn't the typical Hollywood cookie-cutter version so my movie had to be different, specific, and wonderful.

I began to feel that Jenny and I might actually become the people who lived upstairs. The big pool didn't matter anymore—it wasn't essential to the plot. My office and the guest wing fell off the important list. The great room seemed obnoxious. Who the hell was I kidding anyway? Why did I care so much about what Harbor Country thought about me? Worse, why did I build this house to symbolize to them who I really wasn't? Exactly how high was my head up my ass as I directed the construction of this hollow, drywall palace?

What I wrote on that piece of paper was more than documentation, it was a reaffirmation. It was a statement of goals. It was permission to go where my mind would take me, outside the lifestyle-prescribed world we live in.

Are you and your family the stars in your house? Or do you play a supporting role to the limestone? Is the lighting installed to benefit you or the architect's ego? Are you just an extra with a walk-on cameo or does the Vulcan range headline the show?

Here's the real question: Do you maintain your house? Or does it maintain you?

I was finished with this house. Finito! Done! Get me outta here.

RESCUE BATTLE CRY REVIEW

Wall after wall of top-of-the-line cabinetry? Fuck that.

Exactly how high was my head up my ass as I directed the construction of this hollow, drywall palace?

I should have spent the $30,000 for the bathroom on a gold toilet seat. It would have been easier to clean and I could have taken it anywhere.

All that crap is Bengay for the overwhelmed, Dermablend for lifestyles blemished with stress.

I didn't want a bigger deck, I wanted a bigger dick.

Your life is not going to be art you frame with seashells and copper tape that you'll give away at Easter with an attention-starved bottle of homemade bath salts.

Dream kitchen my ass—get a goddamned personal chef.

STEP 2: ANALYZE

THE FIRST EDIT • *n. 1 the initial stripping of anything that isn't absolutely essential to meaningful home life **2** the rebuff of crap **3** phase immediately following crap recognition*

eight

"Call me before you get rid of the club chairs," Wes whispered. Oddly without Bill, he had been cornered into sharing booth fifty-one at Jenny's with House and Garden. It was the Friday night before Thanksgiving, and Harbor Country was bustling with weekend home owners and their guests, either readying their places for the holidays or shutting them down until the following Memorial Day. The restaurant buzzed. Tables were scarce. I gave the dining rooms a quick once-over and determined it was amateur night.

Aimee concurred. "Every Ashley and Dakota is in town to hit the outlets," she whispered wickedly as we stood at the front.

The outlets she referred to in Michigan City were where the townies adorned themselves with the rejected finery of Donna Karan, Burberry, and Ralph Lauren. Many of them passed it off as first quality several times a year at Jenny's, sometimes when a clumsy young bus person had something to do with a dry-cleaning bill that read, "Uncleanable," but mostly to each other as they posed, surveying who was where and with whom.

Wes, House, and Garden had walked in together at eight o'clock. Wes did not have a reservation. Aimee, ever on her toes, promptly offered him booth fifty-one but within earshot of Garden. Try as she did, Aimee was unable to move Wes quickly enough away from the suggestive clutches of House. At least I didn't need to whip up a saccharine exchange while H&G waited for a table, wondering if I knew what I was doing owning a restaurant. It certainly saved the two from having to sit at eighty-one, the least desirable table in the house. It was my unspoken order that this was their corner, so long as Jenny wasn't aware there were available tables in more merciful spots.

"What do you mean you're simplifying?" House pursed her lips at me. "You're going to change Jenny's house?"

"It's a beautiful house," Garden said, touching his tongue to his martini glass. He swilled half of it in one swig.

"I meant what I said about the club chairs," Wes cut in. He poked my shoulder with his finger. "I think it's great that you guys want to do that," he whispered. "Sometimes I say to Bill, *What is all this crap?*"

Now when it came to crap, Wes and Bill were the undisputed queens. Their houses were displayed and merchandised to the G-spot. Theirs was the house on the annual AIDS Benefit Garden Walk, which House toured, taking notes. Wes's wildflower garden seeds actually sprouted, ours didn't even bother germinating. Their water feature was a dug lake with a windmill that was rigged with tiny Italian lights so that from their garden at night, it shone like a miniature Eiffel Tower. When Bill walked into the garden centers, perennial borders from Gary, Indiana, to Buchanan, Michigan, changed. And when Wes and Bill's spectacular Christmas extravaganzas concluded, House became Jewish again.

"You have the most beautiful homes," she gushed to Wes. "You will give me your glass connection in Guadalajara, won't you?"

I didn't say much. It wasn't like I could prove myself worthy of breathing House's lavender-scented air. Wes knew where I was coming from and that was enough.

Jenny joined us a little later. "House," she said, "guess who I talked to this morning?"

"Shoot, honey, who?" said House. She touched her earlobes as she eyed Jenny's, as if to say Are those new?

"Francesca!" Jenny replied.

Francesca was their mutual friend who had recently moved to Maine from New York with her husband, Stuart, to live a simple, uncluttered life on the Midcoast.

House didn't say much else. It was obvious she wasn't a bit interested, especially since Francesca had invited Jenny and me to visit them in Maine and not her and Garden. After another round of drinks and many compliments to Jenny for the sea bass, booth fifty-one disbanded.

"The service was really excellent tonight, Dan," Wes told me generously as he left.

H&G staggered out and flagged a cab. As we did on many Friday nights, Jenny and I arrived home to very happy dogs at around 1:00 am.

At home, every piece of furniture, every table, lamp, painting, vase, artifact, and object had been touched with one of two colors of Post-its. Blue to stay. Yellow to go. I'd started the First Edit, which was painful because it involved taking all the crap, except for nonessential items, out of the house. It hurts to undo something to get to a clean slate, especially in your sanctuary if, indeed, it is.

It will be useful for you to understand why it is so painful. There are three main reasons: (a) money, (b) history, and (c) habit.

MONEY. But I spent good money on that stereo cabinet! I can hear the echoes as I write. I am here to agree with you: Yes! Absolutely! You did spend good money on that stereo cabinet. You spent even more money on that car in your garage you can't wait to replace. As with the car, and unless that stereo cabinet was designed by Eero Saarinen, chances are it is worth considerably less today than when you bought it. The Thigh Master collecting dust under your bed doesn't quite qualify as an asset on your net worth statement. I'm sorry. Believe me, I know how you feel. It is exactly how I felt as I begrudgingly decided what stayed and what went.

Your stuff is worth only what someone else is willing to pay for it. Take the French club chairs: Wes was willing to take them off our hands, but once he got them, he'd be worrying that someone would sit on the arms, or that if he cleaned them too much, the babbling blond twins on the Antiques Roadshow would devalue them to ten dollars.

We take our purchases very personally. Often we are reluctant to face the truth of their monetary value. Most of the contemporary furnishings in our houses hold little relative value. If they were bought new, chances are they aren't worth what you paid for them. Think of it as good news: You won't really be editing out real money. Any real money you recoup will come from the great garage or house sale you will have or from a windfall at a consignment shop.

HISTORY. Everything we've carried over our thresholds into our homes we have loved. Never underestimate this truth.

"I never liked that ugly lamp!" my lawyer friend told me once. But it was convenient when he pursued his love of law - he loved the lamp once, believe me. That's the reason he allowed something so ugly to live on his desk for fifteen years.

There are items in our houses that got there by way of inheritance, things we love more for their histories than for their intrinsic characteristics. How can you part with Granddad's smoky-glass end tables? Mom's four-foot Stiffel lamp with a shade the size of a hamper? Those nesting tables from Crate & Barrel that you bought when you got a promotion?

Remember your definition of who you are, and that your home is the set for your movie. It's not about dad's train set or mom's drop-leaf table, unless you want it to be.

HABIT. Crap happens when we indulge in the whims we are capable of providing. We join the CD club because twelve CDs for one penny is too good to be true. No obligation, right? Just a simple matter of filling out a card indicating your desire to purchase the club's selection of the month. But then it really does become a hassle to respond in time, so why bother? The $16.95 is worth far less than the time it takes to figure out where you put the response card. You indulge yourself. Forward march the unwanted discs.

In my last year of college while contemplating law school I took a job as a legal secretary at Chicago's swankiest divorce firm. People paid hundreds of thousands of dollars to get divorced. I remember so clearly how certain clients would overwhelm themselves with minutae - counting their wives' bathing suits, calculating how many times a week their husbands had dinner in a restaurant without them, etc. They'd subpoena records, and assistant types like me would spend hours charting and tabulating. In the end, they drove themselves crazy because they could.

You are overwhelmed by the demands of your crap because you can afford the luxury of self-indulgence. You think nothing of bringing stuff in, and therefore cannot possibly think of taking stuff out. But you need to take stuff out.

RESCUE ESSENTIAL
THE HOLDING AREA

What you really need is an aircraft hangar, but let's compromise. It is important that you designate a large area, and I do mean large, to serve as a holding area for the fallout that will result as you undertake your First Edit.

A garage is a great place for the Holding Area because it's detached from the rest of the house and presumably your interior traffic patterns won't be interrupted as it gets overloaded. Unless, God forbid, you're one of those people who block off their front door with junk and you go through life entering through the back door.

If the garage itself is in need of a serious editing, don't try to clean it out before you begin editing or you'll never get started. Simply clear as much floor space as you can, allowing safe and clean storage for your things.

If you don't have a garage, then designate another room for the same purpose. Again, don't bother to clean it up before you start your First Edit. It'll all get fixed eventually.

I considered using the guest room for my Holding Area as I put away the stuff with yellow Post-its. It wasn't large enough so I had to use the garage. We had a lot of crap. What I'm saying is, it's OK to change locations midstream so long as crap is hauled into one, and only one, area.

If it seems that all I'm suggesting is easy, or indeed that I went through this massive culling without either Jenny or me throwing a fit, then let me correct that misconception right now. I had to come up with something similar to scream therapy.

But I won't kid you. When we agreed to start the First Edit, Jenny and I did not go through arduous discussions about which opinion mattered the most. I was the clear project leader. Jenny only asked that I was careful with things and not damage them, leaving me solely in charge of our Rescue. That was tremendous support.

If you've been designated the editor in charge, you must feel supported as well. How do you achieve this, knowing full well that others will, at the very least, bitch like you were pulling teeth? First, it is very important that before you start your First Edit there is one leader, the person who has the final word on what goes and what stays. Second, make it a rule that no one can get in the leader's way physically or emotionally when he or she is do-ing the work. Finally, the leader must never ask what others are feeling; he or she will have enough conflicting emotions. There is no need to solicit more anxiety. Just stay the course in polite silence.

Inevitably, a difference of opinion arises if only one opinion counts. Do not underestimate how attached we get to our stuff, even after the decision is made for a radical change. Shit will hit the fan.

What, then, should you do with all these emotions? You're going put them in a place called the Holding Area for Emotions.

RESCUE ESSENTIAL
HOLDING AREA FOR EMOTIONS

A jar or other vessel where ill wishes and bad thoughts that arise during Step II (the First Edit) are placed. These may be handwritten, recorded on tape, or clipped from magazines and taped in the manner of ransom notes. These emotions will be addressed at a later time after you've de-crapped your home, and at your own terms.

This doesn't mean that you have to swallow your feelings and ignore those of your spouse or housemates. It simply means that during Step II of the Rescue, you can only allow the time and energy to acknowledge them which, any therapist will tell you, is plenty. While you must remain committed to addressing these feelings after the physical tasks are over, this is not the time for bitching.

Step I—ASSESSING—is about realizing where you left and the decorator crap took over. Step II is about deconstructing—ANALYZING—the habits that have turned your home into the nonsensical, unrealistic expression that was some decor guru's artistic flatulence. That's why it stinks. You've established a Holding Area for the hard goods. Establish one for matters of the heart. You will sort through both of these areas when the time is appropriate. Addressing each emotion every time it pops up will get in the way of a successful Rescue.

OK, so are you ready to sling some crap? Here's how you prepare:

RESCUE PREP
THE EVE OF DECONSTRUCTION

1. *Have a good meal, but don't get drunk.*

2. *Make sure your Holding Areas are ready.*

3. *Don't think too much except that you're going to haul the crap into one area and one area only.*

4. *Read Chapter 9 before you go to sleep.*

5. *Follow the lists in Chapter 10.*

6. *Don't look back.*

nine

A bedtime story.

So where does crap come from anyway?

Well, it's complicated. Some you buy, some you inherit, and some you just get.

From August to December, Jenny and I didn't speak another word about selling our beloved restaurant. In fact, after suffering my seizure in February, surviving the depression that followed, and coping with the upheaval of home life as we knew it, we were steadied by the restaurant.

Few times since we were married had I thought of how miraculous marriage is, particularly my own. We just worked and squeezed in the rest where we could. That Jenny and I shared a commitment that grew despite the financial, career, and mental cliff-hangers was incredible. Our bliss was inexplicable, particularly in Harbor Country, where the townies considered new ideas a public disturbance, and where marriages were doomed if the bride picked the wrong dress at a Vera Wang sample sale.

This was a woman I had asked two months after moving into our new house, to consider demolishing our new expensive driveway. I'd changed my mind. Now I wanted an approach under an *allée* of monstrous white pines on the opposite side of where the new driveway had been installed. The driveway I proposed stretched over the 1800s approach to the original structure. It was merely a question of revival that Bob Vila posed every week.

"Sure. Got any more stupid ideas?" she said.

"You know nothing!" I responded, my twenty-seven-year-old ego so fragile at the time. I reacted like that a lot in those days. I couldn't be bothered with not marching forward with any reasonably thought-out idea I originated. I was busy all the time, every day, and bulldozed through big decisions at the drop of a hat. Building the house had possessed me with the urgent, annoying self-righteousness of a This Old House host.

"It's a driveway people would kill for," I said. "You've read Fine Gardening. Can't you imagine driving under a canopy of white pines into a courtyard with thick yew hedges and vinca crawling out from under those rhododendrons you had to have?"

I was keeping score, you see, as husbands and wives do when they build houses. You get this if I get that.

"I'm going to work. Are you coming?" she said, remaining utterly unflappable.

We hurried out of the house to our then eighteen-month-old restaurant, located at that point in a leased property, to start a routine sixteen-hour day. In the car I argued my case further.

"Now, listen to me, Jen," I reasoned. "Every great house has an approach. It's a shame to work this hard, have that house on two and a half acres, turn off Fourth Lane onto our driveway, and the front door is right there. I knew from the minute Allen put up that landing the house would be too drywall palace."

"Drywall palace? OK, Kung Fu," Jenny sneered.

"I'm serious! That damn Allen -"

"Now don't you start, Dan," she warned. "Don't blame Allen for your out-of-control change orders."

"Oh, sure!" I said.

"Yes, he's an asshole," she noted. "But you're the one who had to get a fancy project manager from Michigan City. There were plenty of regular general contractors in Harbor Country who'd have done a good job for fear of public shame. But no, you were getting a city socialite."

"But he ate wherever you cooked in Chicago!" I said.

"So?" Jenny said.

"I thought that if he liked you - "

"That he wouldn't be an asshole?" Jenny said. "I feed assholes all the time. He was an asshole when his name was Geraldine O'Malley."

Fucking Allen O'Malley, that son of a bitch transsexual project manager. His name alone could send me into a seizure.

Chicago Hamptonites like Allen who considered themselves erudite in matters of food and wine played a strange and pedantic sport: reading the food section in the Chicago Tribune, stalking chefs, and making as good a personal connection with them as they could so they had a leg up over other townies.

I'd overhear these people all the time at Jenny's say *Did you hear So-and-so Bistro went bankrupt? You know that Chef This-and-that was nabbed for back taxes? I would have loaned him the money, you know. You talk to So-and-so? Sure, all the time.*

When Jenny announced she was dissolving her partnerships, everyone tuned in to watch us move out of the city and up to the lake the way London watched Diana on her final trip to Althorp. Allen and his partner, Alexandria, sent flowers when Jenny's opened; we didn't even know them.

"Loved you in the city, hope you survive out here," the card read.

To their bitter disappointment, Jenny's *tarte tatin* was still the best in the Midwest. But to their greatest surprise, they were about to make a load of money off Jenny herself because of my youthful aspirations.

Shortly after Jenny's opened, a newspaper photographer on assignment from the Chicago Tribune came by unannounced to take our pictures for a feature. Unprepared, I was dressed in Chefwear chili-pepper pants, a T-shirt, and rancid black Dansko clogs. Remember, anyone remotely associated with an eatery at the time dressed this way. It was a bad time for hair, too.

Jenny and Blanche (who later quit washing dishes when she realized cleaning ladies could make twenty-five dollars an hour in Harbor Country) rushed me over to the pot sink. With a torrential swish from the gooseneck, they wet my hair down and rubbed me clean with fresh dishtowels. Jenny ordered me to slap on one of her clean chef coats and we took the picture.

In the following Thursday's food issue, I'd become Jenny's brother, not the real me, her husband/business partner. We couldn't believe it. True,

Jenny does have a brother who is a chef, but mistaking me for him is like confusing Carrie Bradshaw with the Barefoot Contessa.

Predictably, the image of me in a chef's coat stuck in Harbor Country. Some people, like Allen O'Malley, actually thought I cooked, and on that impression alone he held me in his highest esteem. Otherwise I'd just be the guy Jenny married who ruined her career, and I might never, ever have gotten the prestigious O'Malley Project Management, Inc. to build our house.

Allen O'Malley and I sat across from each other at a conference table at the Lakeside Bank and Trust Institution. Its president, Rocky Babbetti, and our loan officer, Mike Jelinek, looked on nervously. Allen was dressed in his usual Polo outlet-center duds, a hybrid of All My Children patriarch and habitual bankruptcy petitioner. He wore ascots and dickeys with crisp white Polo shirts under navy blue blazers that smelled of Brasso mixed with Obsession. Real fuckin' manly.

But Allen was only half the distress. Alexandria was a constant presence, making sure I realized that Allen was The Man and I—hah-hah!—a nonchef!

Alexandria O'Malley-whatever-her-name-was looked like Dan Rather, except Dan was prettier. She was somewhat notorious, so revealed the whispers between the tables at Jenny's Restaurant. Whisperers said Alexandria bragged that her clothes were bought first quality from Donna Karan in Chicago. Other whisperers indicated that Alexandria was keenly possessed of unmatched outlet-shopping prowess on the lake side of Interstate 94. Alexandria had the goods no sooner than they fell off the truck. Whisperers said that though her wardrobe seemed like it was bought downtown, *Look at the snipped labels.*

"Where on earth do you get this information?" Jenny would laugh.

"I hear it on the floor all the time!" I'd say. No one else, however, heard it, but it was not like I was making these things up. I'm from Guam. We hear things.

Rocky Babbetti had summoned Allen and me to the bank that morning after Allen phoned him about a fax I had sent to his office. It read, "Don't fuck with me, Cowgirl." I fed it into the fax machine, taping both ends together so that he got the message over and over again.

I did it because we were eight months into our building project and all construction had ceased. The hiss of a pneumatic hose hadn't been heard on the site for three weeks. It was late autumn, and a two-week rainstorm had caused the subfloor in the great room to buckle and pucker. Allen O'Malley's crew of numbskulls was halfway done sheeting the roof when they decided to take an unexplained break.

I was extremely pissed off. It was my first drywall palace, after all.

"You're quite the writer, Dan. I had no idea," Allen remarked. He eyed Rocky and Mike to muster disdain. "You need to watch your language, boy."

Boy?

"Rocky," I spoke firmly, "you sent an inspector out there to look at the progress. What did he say?"

"He quit to work at the new Home Depot," Rocky said nervously. "We've been looking to replace him for six weeks."

Mike the loan officer had only been mildly involved, but he perked up and looked at Rocky. "He's at Home Depot now? Damn, I hear they have a great employee discount."

"We could use it, hey?" Rocky replied, relieved by the comical exchange.

Well I could have cared less about an employee discount, never mind that, in the middle of my house-building woes, my banker and builder paused for a moment of awe over a job switch that required an id badge and apron. "But the great room is open to the sky!" I interjected loudly. "The subfloor is puckering from the rain. Let's go over there right now! Rocky, he's not doing his damn job!"

I was boiling. Precariously close to blurting out some incoherent native cackling, I glared at Allen and brought out the silent, big killer. Slowly I looked him up and down the way enemies did on *Dynasty*. (We practiced that look a lot on Guam when I was a kid. War dances had been obsolete for centuries.)

Allen reacted violently as though somehow my eyes had turned every one of the snipped tags lying against his pale, wrinkled body into red-hot irons. He rose from his seat.

"Do you think I don't know that you tried to poison me, Tahiti Boy?" he bellowed.

Tahiti Boy?

"Go to hell!" I responded in my best John Forsythe. Rising, I gave the conference-room table a clumsy slap with my sweaty palms. I eructated an Aaron Spelling-sized Go fuck yourself.

Then it got real ugly for 20 minutes. Both kinds of testosterone, natural and synthetic, bombarded across the conference table. It was like a bar brawl in Gunsmoke. Talks broke down when Allen felt compelled to stand up and grab his crotch with both hands in an ill-executed Mafioso threat, and I started to laugh in uncontrolled hysteria.

Two weeks later the restaurant's linen service was running late. So I rushed to Sook's Dry Cleaners in Michigan City, Indiana, where I ran into Alexandria, as earnest as a prime-time anchorman, consulting with Mariah Sook over an outlet-fresh Donna Karan camel coat in great need of being de-pilled. Now that was a Dynasty moment if there ever was one. Allen's bitch was busted. Already, I could see myself conducting the symphony of whispers at Jenny's.

Feeling quite smug, I drove from Sook's to the building site to have a look, perhaps a canary-eating wink at Allen. But it had been abandoned in obvious haste, as though, indeed, they were running in shame. Allen and company had left behind a rather comprehensive scaffolding system and a very large, very heavy air compressor.

Thus began our accumulation of crap at the house in Harbor Country. More crap would accumulate under different, no less twisted circumstances, when you consider that throughout the 1990s, France, Italy, Spain, and Bali waged a war in catalogues and magazines that was fought by citizen soldiers like you and me. Italy won, by the way, according to Wes and Bill.

For years I kept Allen's goods as both trophy and hostage, wishing for the day he'd come crawling down the second driveway in his old high heels, making nice for his compressor. I fantasized about him begging at my feet for the scaffolding so that he could install some crappy faux verdigris weather vane at some other drywall palace. That didn't happen. Instead, the scaffolding and compressor got buried behind the bequests of dead in-laws and load after load of crap debris.

The thought crossed my mind to dump the compressor and scaffolding on Allen's and Alexandria's front lawn (with its purple mulch) and set them ablaze. Of course I didn't do it. It would have taken a monumental effort to clear a path to them in my garage in the first place.

Jenny would never have allowed it. She kept me in line, patiently nudging me toward the mature restaurateur I was quickly to become. Her husband and business partner, no matter the opinions. In sickness and in health. For richer or poorer. For what lay ahead.

ten

THE KITCHEN
What stays

APPLIANCES
Stove w/oven, gas preferably
Refrigerator/freezer
Dishwasher
Microwave
Handheld mixer or KitchenAid

ACCESSORIES & UTENSILS
1 wooden cutting board for fruits and vegetables
1 large plastic cutting board for meats and fish
2 sets of mixing bowls
3 wooden spoons for mixing
2 wire whisks
2 rubber spatulas
3 large serving spoons
3 large serving forks
3 hinged tongs
1 set of measuring spoons
1 set of measuring cups
1 glass measuring pitcher

POTS & PANS
1 sixteen-quart pot for stock and boiling
1 five-quart pot for stews and braising
1 cast-iron skillet

1 medium sauce pan
1 small sauce pan
1 nonstick fry pan
1 rectangular roaster, glass
1 rectangular roaster, metal w/rack
3 cookie sheets
2 round cake pans
2 glass pie pans

DISHES & SERVING PIECES
1 set of your best dishes, including coffee service
3 serving bowls
2 serving trays
2 glass or ceramic pitchers

GLASSWARE
1 set of glass tumblers
1 set of wineglasses (suitable for red or white)
1 set of champagne flutes
1 set of cocktail (highball) glasses

SILVERWARE & CUTLERY
1 set of your best silver or flatware
best set of kitchen knives you have

PLASTIC/STORAGE
1 set of freezer storage Tupperware-type containers

The rest of the items in your kitchen must be relocated immediately to
the Holding Area.

DINING ROOM

Unfortunately, modern living has made traditional dining rooms
indoor garages or first-floor basements. Rarely have I ever seen a dining
room uncluttered. People just don't eat in them anymore. In fact, they
avoid them. It seems fitting that they've become the walk-in junk drawer
of our time.

On the bright side, editing your dining room is a pretty
straightforward venture because it involves clearing out anything that is
unrelated to eating. Sideboards, china cabinets, and side chairs can stay

along the wall. At the center should be a dining table with a clean surface except for a centerpiece, a pair of candlesticks with a bowl, etc. There can be a tablecloth; however, it should not cover any kind of required repair work as it only keeps the "to do" list you can't get to longer than it needs to be. Get the table fixed, refinished, whatever. End of story.

CHINA CABINET: More than any other room in a traditionally laid-out home, a dining room most effectively displays heirlooms. These deserve to remain undisturbed during the First Edit, provided you figure out a way to keep the bulk of them in cabinets and off surfaces. Old delicate things handed down from generation to generation belong in china cabinets, yet you should be aware that these collections can also benefit from editing. Can you pass some on to other family members? Consider hanging large platters and antique plates on the wall where they will be readily appreciated, out of the way, and easy to dust. But don't feel compelled to toss all of it out because you are too eager to edit. The funny thing is, the more old stuff behind glass, the better. Nothing looks worse than an empty china cabinet unless it's one filled with new stuff bought expressly for the purpose of display.

Family heirlooms include, but are not limited to, candlesticks, china, extra silver (most of which should be used daily and serve as the only set in the home), bowls, fancy platters, and vases. A word about vases: You should have one vase for every table surface; that is, if you have a total of five tables in your home, you need only five vases. Keep your best ones and resist keeping ones for "what if" arrangements. There is no good reason to keep a three-gallon glass bowl in case you get around to buying the six dozen roses it was designed to hold. Six dozen roses at forty dollars a dozen? Please. Even if you get flowers cheap, you throw them away. Why not spend the money on a better vase?

BUFFET/DRESSER BASE: This provides storage for table linens, which should consist of the best tablecloths in your lot, and napkins that number twice the amount of chairs that fit around your dining table. It's also a place to store candles.

REMINDER: Fight the urge to "return" the misplaced items you find in each room as you edit. If an item is in a wrong room, it means something: It doesn't belong where you thought it did in the first place. If it still feels out of place in the room where you find it, it probably shouldn't have been acquired at all. Don't bother with figuring all this out. It is very important that you concentrate on taking unnecessary items directly into the Holding Area.

LIVING ROOM

I've decided that it is called a living room for an obvious reason - it's alive. Every living organism is built with a profound degree of symmetry, an evenness. Living rooms ought to be similarly laid out: a spine (central axis), limbs, and—oh, all right— a head or "focal point" (for you who watch too much HGTV).

Imagine your living room as having a real physical anatomy, even that the furniture placement is like a Lego model of you in a state of repose reading a book. Your head and back are the sofa and your arms are two chairs. Your feet are a fireplace or picture window. The book you're reading is a low table or rug (maybe both) in front of the sofa and between the armchairs. In real life a quiet moment doesn't include piles of books and papers, tchotchkes, etc. It's just you on a blanket with a book.

If imagining your living-room arrangement as a living thing is too difficult, think about this: When Hawaiians look at mountains they see the goddess Pele; when children look at clouds they see all kinds of animals. Even you've seen the man in the moon. Go ahead and find what I'm suggesting in your living room. Don't be such a stick-in-the-mud. You imagine you're Madonna every time "Ray of Light" comes on the radio, so who the hell do you think you're kidding?

I can't tell you how much seating you need to have in your living room. I hate to emphasize seating, as often it is given importance while table surfaces are neglected. A room full of the world's most comfortable chairs and sofas is useless if they alone compose a living room. A good rule of thumb is eighteen inches of running table surface for every seating area that can accommo date one person comfortably. For example: You decide to leave a standard-size sofa and two armchairs, which gives a comfortable seating capacity of five. You should have 90 inches of running table surface, which could equate to two 18-inch side tables and one 104-inch sofa or coffee table, or however you wish to divide it.

THE ONLY ITEMS THAT SHOULD BE LEFT IN THE LIVING ROOM ARE TABLES AND SEATING (sofas and chairs). All else, including lamps, rugs, and paintings on the wall, needs to be relocated to the Holding Area.

BEDROOMS

Bedrooms present less of a Rescue challenge than other rooms, provided hard surfaces are clutter free. Nightstands need to be cleared of everything but a lamp, an alarm clock, a telephone, and medication, if necessary. Note: You are also allowed to keep a book and other personal things but keep them contained in a basket for a while until you really get that tops of dressers cannot be repositories for things that have or will become dusty.

A bed, nightstand(s), two lamps, and one dresser/armoire per person are the basic furniture for a bedroom. Chairs, chaise longues, and love seats require serious consideration. I know, I know—we see them on TV and in magazines all the time, but, really, how many home owners do you know who hang out in their bedrooms when they're not actually in bed? Chairs, desks, etc. are useful only for children and/or writers who need to be available for their muses. Everything else needs to be taken to the Holding Area.

Bedrooms also contain the dreaded closet. This can make editing a bit problematic. My closet (and Jen's, God knows) was filled with things I didn't wear. I wish I could say that it was difficult to start sorting through the clothes but, in all honesty, it was the simplest part of my whole First Edit.

For now, leave the clothes and proceed with the rest of Step II.

BATHROOMS

For years the American bathroom has done double duty. Bottom line, bathrooms are for bathing and relieving yourself. If you remember this, half the battle of uncluttering your bathroom will be won.

Are you someone who looks for candlelit healing experiences in a bathtub with a glorious view of the commode? It's not exactly like watching a soothing tank of sea horses, if you know what I mean. The current trend of turning the bathroom into a temple spa is exactly the kind of bullshit that gets out of control. Think about it. We are adding scraping wax drippings off the tub to the already dreaded duty of scrubbing the toilet. Are we crazy? Stop it now!

Chances are your bathroom is chock-full of beauty products and a hair dryer, which horrifies me, given that electricity and water have long been a deadly mix. I suggest that outside the actual fixtures, your bathroom contain only these items:

SHOWER/BATHTUB: One bar of soap, one bottle of bubble bath, shampoo, conditioner, rubber squeegee, washcloth/back brush.

SINK/VANITY: Hand soap (liquid soap in a pump is great) and a box of Kleenex. If there is a cabinet below, store extra toilet tissue and feminine products only—NO CLEANING PRODUCTS OR MATERIALS.

MEDICINE CABINET: Razors, toothbrush, toothpaste, and first-aid items including over-the-counter medicines like aspirin, muscle rubs, etc. Prescription medication should never be kept in a medicine cabinet that has public access. Instead, these should be kept in a private place accessible only to those who are prescribed them. Your ailments are not public information.

Everything else, including hair dryers, curling irons, curlers, etc., should be relocated to the Holding Area, where they will find their way to proper Reintegration (Rescue Step III).

BASEMENTS

Unless a basement or some portion of it is actually finished, its primary role is mechanical room, plain and simple. A house that is built on a slab has a mechanical room. This is usually a closet with a furnace and water heater in it. On a wall somewhere else in the house is a circuit breaker box. I can't imagine a mechanical closet being used for storage. In truth, this is probably rarely done because the safety issue is so obvious. Yet storing boxes of stuff in a basement carries the exact mind-set as if you were wedging them between a furnace and water heater. Mechanical rooms are mechanical rooms. Basements are usually bigger, that's all.

If you have an older home, chances are the washer and dryer are in the basement. Additionally, if you are a hobby enthusiast of some sort the basement is the logical place to set up shop. These are two of a handful of acceptable uses for an unfinished basement.

Storage, on the other hand, can get tricky because we often say we're "storing something in the basement" when that something has failed to be useful to us. It's junk.

However, there are items that are "actively stored" in basements, things that are used regularly within the calendar year like holiday decorations, camping gear, etc. These can stay.

Not quite junk, "passively stored" items like the chain saw you won two years ago in a raffle that you haven't yet used because you live in a townhouse, or the NordicTrack that pisses you off, have to go. Passively stored items include good old clothes, records, and old electronic things. They need to be removed and placed in the Holding Area. They will eventually end up in a house sale or at Goodwill.

ATTIC

Attics differ little from basements except they are usually clear of mechanicals, save ductwork and wires. However, these spaces (again) tend to be repositories for active storage and passive storage. Remove items that are passively stored and take them to the Holding Area.

FAMILY ROOM/MEDIA ROOM

Leave it the way it is for now. It is the one room, the remaining vestige of your previously overwhelming home, that is allowed to remain as is. You have to relax, after all. You've just turned your world upside down. But remember—unlike with the rest of your house, which has undergone veritable pillage, leave everything in this room contained. Don't let the stuff move anywhere and contaminate your hard work. At least, not yet.

RESCUE WISDOM

1. GET OUT OF THE HOUSE. You won't recognize it. It's going to depress you. You will resent everything (especially me).

2. A RESCUE TAKES TIME. Think of all the time (and money) it took you to create the Styling Chore Hell in the first place. Life without that kind of pressure doesn't happen immediately.

3. CLING TO FAMILIAR REFUGE. In other words, drink. Or work your life away as you always have. But that'll change, too.

4. REAL FRIENDSHIP WILL REVEAL ITSELF. Some friends will call you crazy and alienate themselves from the entire process and you. Their own insecurities will drive them to point out how ridiculously you are behaving by de-crapifying your life. Feel sorry for them later, but in the meantime tell them to go to hell.

eleven

Alexandria called sometime during Christmas week to make New Year's Eve reservations. She and Allen hadn't set their men's size 12s in Jenny's in over four years.

"Dan!" Alexandria chirped, "Allen and I would like to come for the last seating New Year's Eve! Have you got a table?"

"Hello?" I said, a bit unsure.

"It's Alexandria O'Malley," she said "Do you have a table at the last seating?"

I looked at the reservations. The restaurant was booked. The only two extra chairs were at eighty-one which was a four top. Aimee had already given it to House and Garden.

Why was she calling?

"I've only got one table, Alexandria, near the bathroom in the back dining room," I said dutifully.

"We'll take it," she said brightly.

"Best to Allen," I said. I hung up the phone mildly flabbergasted. *What was up with her?*

I crossed out H&G and wrote in the O'Malleys. Aimee would catch it later, scold me, and then call Alexandria to apologize for my mistake. By then all the restaurants within a fifty-mile radius would be booked and the O'Malleys would be screwed. Perfect. Or maybe Aimee would forget altogether and H&G would have to wait for an unlikely opening and eat uncomfortably at the bar. Perfect.

New Year's Eve looked great on the floor, but was hell behind the scenes, as per usual. The head dishwasher appeared to be high on pot, the espresso machine exploded a couple of times, and we ran out of bread plates because the townies were requesting more olive oil than normal for dipping the free bread.

At some point, the sauces on the dessert plates were coming out in puddles. I went back to investigate and found that one of pastry ladies, Joycelin, a nice woman in her late fifties from the Upper Peninsula, had peed on herself while sneezing. She was waiting, embarrassed, in the employee bathroom for her husband to bring her clean pants. In her absence, a harried waiter suggested to one of the dishwashers that he plate up the desserts.

I took over for about thirty minutes until Joycelin was back in shape. Jenny gave her husband a bottle of champagne when he came with the clean panties. "That's for later, for you two," she told him, disappearing behind the cook's line.

At the front, Aimee was rushing a thirty-something couple to the bathrooms. They were about to puke after discreetly inhaling contraband cigars in the lounge. The man didn't make it and hurled all over a urinal. His date had to revive him in their white stretch limo, whose driver was nowhere to be found.

Outside, cars parked pell-mell around the limo and spilled neatly onto the old road to Detroit. This slight but expected inconvenience aggravated the already excited townies piling into Jenny's. The restaurant was bursting and anything that was slightly off the plan made the patrons extremely angry.

The diners were the usual suspects, individuals I knew by face either from the restaurant or casually about town. They'd smile at me and make small talk while we waited in line to pay for bath salts and organic T-shirts at a shop in Lakeside. We'd chitchat about the rise in property taxes or a new house under construction while buying flats of annuals at the Wal-Mart in Michigan City. Generally, these were people who didn't mind waiting eternities at a Jo-Ann's store for fabrics or The Christmas Tree Shoppe for the right raffia or bag of Spanish moss for their matching ivy topiary balls. But there was something about going out for dinner in Harbor Country, something perhaps about New Year's Eve itself. People were upset when they weren't seated right on time and said out loud that Jenny's was a fucked-up place run by amateurs.

At one point a man angrily introduced himself as an attorney "from Chicago." He stomped up to me to ask to speak with the owner.

"I'm an owner," I said. "What seems to be the problem?"

"I don't know who the hell you think you are," he said angrily. "I want to speak with Jenny."

"I'm Jenny's husband. I am an owner," I repeated. "What can I do for you?"

He was seething.

"I know Oprah's chef," he warned. "And I want you to know that I know a lot of people who eat out all the time who won't like that I've waited 10 minutes for my table."

"I'm sorry," I apologized. "You know how New Year's Eve is; people are taking their time -"

"Are you going to get Jenny or what?" he said loudly.

He moved closer. He was really out of sorts.

"Obviously she can't speak with you right now," I said slowly, suggesting by my tone to back off.

"Well, you tell her I said that you people don't know what the fuck you're doing!" he said.

He stormed back to his wife who was waiting at the bar cursing about me to those who would listen. They simmered quietly in their disgust, looking quite dangerous in factory store cashmere.

Just your normal New Year's Eve, I said to myself.

"How's it going?" Aimee said humming, her adrenaline running high.

"Remind me next year to charge ten thousand dollars per head, will you?" I said. "Are you all set with the cigar aficionados?" I was pumped up myself. Self-righteous bastards who introduced themselves with "from Chicago" after their names did that to me. They were like EpiPens.

"Ugh! He puked a pound of lime pulp!" she said. She looked at the attorney couple seated at the bar. "What's up with Chik-n-Dick over there? Do they have a reservation?"

"Ten minutes ago. You know they're gonna get us on Oprah's next Worst-of show," I replied flatly.

"I'm setting up their table right now," Aimee said.

"Well, fuck you very much," I sputtered mocking the attorney's wife. I spoke under my breath with a straight face since the atrocity victims, absolutely beside themselves, stared right at me.

"Ooh!" Aimee cried. "I'll make sure they get extra cheese on everything!"

"Tell Jenny to break out the olive oil reserves. They're gonna go off Atkins just to spite me!"

My words faded into the strains of Prince's "1999" while Aimee moved to escort them to their table.

As I stood watching for the room to turn over, I spotted bus teams I could tap for quick resets. A booth was breaking up. I started toward the head of their party for their coat-check ticket so I could quickly get them out of the building. Then Allen and Alexandria O'Malley walked in.

Aimee rushed to the front. "Happy New Year!" she said brightly.

"Hello!" they sang in unison. Allen wore a silver ascot and looked around excitedly, adjusting his ping-pong balls.

"It looks really busy," Alexandria said loudly, with a hint of surprise. She gave Allen her coat. While he checked it, she posed for me, feigning exasperation. She wore a black dress solid to the bust. Above it, the sleeves, décolletage and back were a sheer fabric.

"Dan!" she exclaimed looking me up and down.

"Alexandria!" I said, honestly breathless.

"How do I look?" she asked, blinking.

Like pasta in fucking squid ink I said to myself behind a waxy grin.

Aimee cleared her throat. "It's the usual New Year's Eve," she told them quickly. "Your table is ready. Come with me."

I watched them walk to eighty-one. Aimee pressed the okay sign to her back. I noticed that sitting in eighty was a couple in their fifties with new-born twins strapped to their chests. The infants' accoutrement spilled onto the O'Malleys' table. (Harbor Country had been experiencing a baby boom in recent years among the 50+ crowd.) The O'Malley's experience would be terrifically horrible. Perfect.

I eagerly awaited the glorious moment when I could tell House that she'd have to sit her fat ass on a barstool for the night. But, as it turned out, the cigar aficionados decided to forfeit their table and it went to H&G.

A&A ate, keeping their eyes on me to see when I walked past their table. I tried to put off that inevitability all night, but finally I had to do it. I needed to get to the other side.

Alexandria stuck her arm out. Her triceps quivered like Alfred Hitch-cock's bottom lip. "So are you guys moving, Dan?" she gargled.

"No," I said, shrugging. "What ever gave you that idea?"

"I was taking some clients around to see my work," Allen said, "and we noticed you were emptying the house."

Alexandria smiled smugly and looked around. "This is a nice building, Dan," she said. "It must have cost a fortune."

Allen gave me a once-over like he'd just bought my interest in Denver-Carrington right out from under me. "Hey," he said patronizingly, "the res-taurant business is hard. The best people don't make it. At least you had a few good years."

It took all I had not to say *You know, you're right, Allen. Restaurants are like construction—no place for pussies.*

Sometime around midnight Jenny and I found each other. By two o-clock we were home. Unlike the New Year's morning the year before, the house was cavernous. After the First Edit it had all the charm of a time-share, I have to admit. But now it seemed full of promise, as though we'd just moved into it.

A fire roared in the Rumford. We cuddled on a couch. The dogs lay at our feet and the sparks echoed. "Do you know what my New Year's resolution is?" I said to Jenny.

"What's that?"

"To shrink this place somehow."

Jenny didn't answer. She had fallen asleep. I could see a faint smile of relief at the corners of her mouth.

RESCUE CELEBRATION
NEW YEAR'S EVE 101

1. BRING EXTRA PANTIES. You really could pee on yourself.

2. BRING EXTRA DIAPERS. You will pee on yourself if your midlife crisis plan includes a newborn.

3. EXTRA ASCOT. Not silver. Try a little dickey, for once.

4. TIP GENEROUSLY. Always give the help champagne, and the limo driver his choice of dessert.

5. CURB RUDENESS. Especially if you're in factory-store cashmere. It's the end of the year, not the end of the world.

twelve

Jenny's was famous for a dish we called Thai Style Chilean Sea Bass, a preparation Jen developed in our old location when the fish was cheap—before the height and the hype. A little-touted fact about Chilean sea bass is that it is frozen shortly after it is harvested in South America. By the time it reaches consumers, it's anybody's guess how long it has been frozen, or how many ways it has been creatively refreshed.

Every food column in print and every food guru on television was proclaiming at the time that all fish should be ordered rare, period. Of course, every diner in Harbor Country repeated the mantra. Jenny urged the waitstaff to encourage their tables not to order the fish rare, but the suggestion was met with, "I've been to Chile. Chilean Sea Bass is supposed to be rare."

Well, the fish tasted like shit when served rare. Especially to the middle-American palate. It is oily and dense, more like mackerel than whitefish. But you couldn't tell that to the Harbor Country townies. They'd just learned to pronounce buffalo mozzarella.

Plate after plate of Chilean sea bass grilled to the requested rare came back into Jenny's kitchen. We were undeservedly getting criticism for fish that wasn't what the gurus promised. It was a problem. But Jenny was on it.

She always loved the caramelized, practically overcooked fried fish preparations of Thai cuisine. Understanding that Thai flavor combinations are highly addictive, she simply put the two together and developed Thai

Style Chilean Sea Bass. The fish had to be cooked a long time (in fact, it was cooked twice) to achieve the sweet-sour tamarind glaze.

Well, Harbor Country loved it. They convinced themselves that, now many times past rare, the sea bass was cooked perfectly. The Food Network came to Michigan and featured it. Travel & Leisure photographed it. Zagat put us in their guides.

And then one day, the restaurant received a call from a field editor of a magazine that we'd never heard of. She wanted to photograph Jenny in her dream home kitchen, cooking the now fabled sea bass. The request couldn't have come at a worse time—by now the photo opportunities were long gone.

For about a month I avoided the Holding Area like it was a nudist beach. You will, too. Perhaps you should. Generally, I walked around in complete denial of my Rescue, staring into space, secretly test-driving my writer's imagination. Finally, on a warm day at the end of January 1999, I took a long, dazed look at the Holding Area. I could barely speak, the mass was enormous. In fact, I could hardly hear. I know this because Blanche claimed she'd been right in front of me, calling out a full three minutes before I snapped out of apparent delirium.

"What?" I blurted. I was confused and irritated as though I had been abruptly shaken from a sound sleep.

"For the tenth time! " she shouted. "What are you? A ballerina boy?"

"Wha—huh?" I stammered, in awkward arabesque.

I had removed the last box of crap from inside the house in a heightened state of movie-making determination. When I put it down, I came across a childhood memory I had long buried. A brown box.

In it lay a shriveled pair of boxing gloves previously owned by an Enola Gay mechanic stationed on Guam during the war. Some fifty years later, like the mummified kidneys of a great giant salvaged from a postwar sideshow, the gloves rested on yellowed pages of the Pacific Daily News. They reported that a local girl had been crowned Miss World after nude pictures of the real winner, Miss Germany, ran in Penthouse magazine. 1980. That was the year

I became Guam's lone representative to the men's Olympic figure-skating competition in Lake Placid.

I was barely thirteen years old and as unaware of the sport itself as I was the absurdity of my situation. But when the chief summons the warrior, the brave presents himself, abandoning his current occupation. In my case, I simply had to drop the chicken drumstick I was gnawing on, turn off The Benny Hill Show, and tiptoe around the life-sized crucifix where Jesus' dying eyeball followed me. Shortly thereafter, I stepped onto the ice at Pedro's Ice Plant and fell on my ass. My flip-flops slid across the ice like bouquets of roses fleeing the scene.

The whole notion of Guam participating in the Winter Olympics started innocently enough as idle gossip. A little chismiss, as they say. The Wagging Tongue: Sister Benjamin Moore Gumataotao. A blood relative. It is important that I tell you about these relatives.

Her grandmother's name was Sutcha, meaning "sugar." Sutcha Ho was my grandfather's oldest sister. (Unfortunate as Auntie Sutcha's burden may seem, the bitter prize actually belongs to Grandfather's third wife, S'kankee, a Maori by way of Celebes.)

From 1976 to 1978, Sister Lia, as Sister Benjamin Moore Gumataotao was known in the village, spent two years in Minneapolis on an exchange nun program with the Daughters of St. Paul, they of the Publishing Pauls, the graphically gifted virgins responsible for all the hymnals, novena booklets, and catechism instruction books distributed throughout the Roman Catholic empire. It was in Minneapolis that Sister Lia heard of a large family from Tonga, the Wolfgrams, whose talented children would end up topping the U.S. singles charts as the Jets with pop hits like "Crush on You." There was to be much gold for the Tongans. There would be no such metal for Guam.

People on Guam like to have sex, or, as they say in the village, they like to drown their pet cats. Sexual intercourse. The pure old-fashioned kind with a lot of body fluid and drama. The if-I-can't-have-you-no-one-can kind. It's unusual, actually, that I'm my mother's only child in what continues to be a prophylactic-free coast. Mother was one of fourteen children born in twelve years to her namesake (Rosa), who breast-fed every one of my aunties and uncles. My earliest remembrance of Grandmother was that her boobs dropped clear down to her waist. Understandable, yes, but a trait that was shared by my uncles.

The only picture we have of Grandmother at a relatively young age is one that was published in Life magazine. She is surrounded by my young aunts and uncles. It appears as though my Uncle Rudy (the oldest) has his arm draped over her shoulder the way most "natives" pose for pictures. The photograph was taken in 1946, a heady time right after the Japanese occupation that the old people don't like to talk about. It was a period when their near decimation was seemingly neglected as the island went from Japanese concentration camp immediately into a staging area for General MacArthur's final blows and reglorification efforts in the Pacific Rim.

By 1946, all of Grandmother's children were already born and should have been in the picture. So no one could figure out why Mother's fraternal twin, Miguel, was missing in the photograph. In 1990 I took a closer look at the photo, which had been hanging in the same dark corner for years in Grandmother's house, and I discovered what turned out to be a pair of very wide, very contented eyes camouflaged between Grandmother's and Uncle Rudy's matching polka-dot shirts (everybody's clothes were made from the same bolt of fabric). I'd found Uncle Miguel! And the arm draped over Grandmother's left shoulder, which we had believed all these years belonged to Uncle Rudy, was actually her left breast. An apparently very hungry Miguelito had hoisted it over her shoulder and around her neck, nursing on it while the Life photographer was setting up the shot. Mother confirmed that they all snacked that way up to a certain age before learning the nutritious joys of chicken.

I guess I always knew Grandmother's breasts were much talked about, her native nickname was Chai Susu (meaning Rose with the Boobs). I also knew that one of the connotations of her nickname was that she had had her share of lovers, or as they say, her cat could hold its breath for a long time. The elasticity part, however, blew me away

Sister Lia, proud Ho that she was, slung her own tits around, sleeping exclusively with the highest and most powerful political officials, except for a weak moment when she bedded a Capuchin bisexual (who also slept with Uncle Miguel). Shortly after she returned from Minneapolis, she took the governor, Paulo Clavio, to be her lover. One evening after drowning her pet cat repeatedly, Sister Lia whispered into the governor's ear. This is something all island men love; whispers are the best way to get our undivided attention and we are profoundly sensitive to them. Sister Lia was especially good at it whispering. Sweet nothings about being cold in Minneapolis, so cold that her nipples were constantly beetle nuts. Something about this, something about that, something about Tongan children who could sing and dance and were getting a recording contract with Arista.

Governor Clavio sat up.

"Tongans?" he boomed. "What the hell can those Tongans do that we can't do better? We're Guamanians!"

He got out of bed and mumbled, motioning to Sister Lia to get dressed and leave.

Thereafter, Sister Lia's pet cat would not drown for some time. Obsessed with getting one of our people a recording contract, the governor spent night and day combing the island for nightingales who might cross over to the American Top Forty, refusing any contact with the woman who had brought such devastating news to him. His search was futile. The traditional Guamanian singing voice is beyond even a Sting or Paul Simon collaboration. So he settled for the next best thing: a Roller Derby team he named the Mighty Brown Snakes, after our well-known pests.

And a bit about the snakes.

Boiga irregularis, the New Guinea tree snake, was brought to the island sometime during World War II and, like Sister Lia's gossip about the Tongans, ended up becoming a problem of gargantuan proportions. The snake devoured every native bird species and was finding its way into plumbing pipes—once into the toilet at my house while Mother was reading the Guinness Book of World Records. (The snake was large and thrashed wildly. The noise was so loud it was misidentified as a drowning cat and summarily ignored.)

Eventually the Roller Derby team was disbanded when the governor was informed that our skates were not standard-issue for the sport. We all used the metal clip-on style, which he preferred because they looked really islandy. Like Tevas on wheels. Unable to present the world a Roller Derby team in traditional island dress, he gave up on one-upping the Tongans and became a sullen, inaccessible man.

Sister Lia's pet cat screamed constantly for a drowning, making her hiss sweet-nothing stories out loud at the governor in open corridors and across public halls but to no avail. She screamed whispers! This troubled even the old chiefs, who wondered delightedly out loud if he was homosexual. Finally, the sister cousin was forced to make a very public display of her horny scorn.

At the Annunciation fiesta in the capital village, she blurted out one of her Minneapolis remembrances as the governor walked onto a dais to observe a basket-making dance.

"Hey you, big man!" she cried, wresting a megaphone from a prayer leader.

"The cousin of Peggy Fleming taught me how to use the big stapler in Minnesota!" she cried. "It was blessed by the pope, you dig?"

"Lord, hear our prayer," the crowd answered.

A few old women looked at each other and crossed their eyes at the strange psalm. Then suddenly, as though God himself had intervened, the governor's fighting spirit returned. He looked at Sister Lia. She looked at him. Their eyes locked in a steamy gaze. He excused himself, Sister excused herself, and off they went.

Many still believe that Sister Lia's invocation of the pope was what did it for the governor, but really it was Peggy Fleming.

That afternoon, the Governor resolved that Guam would have its Olympic representative. In a very swift island-wide search co-conducted by an ex-hockey player from the navy base, my feet were determined to be less flat than those of the rest of the young people had been previously determined to be able to pull off a single lutz.

After eighteen months of training at Pedro's Ice Plant, learning my school figures and an artistic program to the theme from Rocky (ergo the boxing gloves), I was sent off to Lake Placid to seek my Olympic glory. I was able to perform my figures and the sketchy routine with relative aplomb inside the ice plant. However, amid the excitement of my being able to stick an otherwise horrible flying camel, I was never informed (nor had it even been considered) that an Olympic ice rink was bigger than our entire village square, never mind Pedro's Ice Plant. I dropped my foot in the figures and performed the long program in the corner of the ice rink at Lake Placid. What could I do? I left as I came. Last.

"What?" I blurted, in arabesque.

Blanche was laughing, hardly able to stand up straight.

"Jenny wants you to call her," she laughed. "I seen you doin' that ballet move in the walk-in cooler last week, lettin' the fan blow your hair back and shit," she chortled.

I dialed Jenny at the restaurant.

"What magazine?" I said, trying to brush off the growing fear that, fuck it, a staff member had yet another reason to snicker about me behind my back. Why couldn't I have just been caught sleeping in front of a computer like a real writer?

"They want to take my picture for a July issue," she said. "Something about me in my kitchen. I don't really know, they were vague."

"What the fuck!" I said, "No fucking way; the house is a mess!"

"Well, should I tell them I'm not interested in doing it then?" Jenny said. "I don't care either way. It's not like saying no to the homeless. You decide, OK?"

Decide whether I wanted some good free press? For days I waffled between yes and no, tortured. But I wasn't quite ready to invite the world into our home in the middle of its Rescue. How I agonized.

Finally, I said yes. But I held fast and decided not to disturb the newly edited house and to leave my process intact. I just figured they'd take a picture of Jenny in the kitchen, which we could set up for the shot. But it wasn't to be. The photographer came and left, unable to take the photograph she was hoping for in a house she'd been told had been styled to the hilt. A swift bit of chitchat went around the town and into Chicago that we were going under and were selling off the contents of the house.

Alexandria called in February to book a small dining room for a company party. "Aren't you glad I called?" she chirped. "I heard you could use the business!"

I was too weary and witless to make reference to Allen O'Malley Project Management LLC's third reorganization as I meekly booked their party, or even to voice my suspicions that she was involved in some mischief. While every February before 1999 had passed sleepily in the Snow Belt, it was double-shot caffeinated that year. It was like Evita's funeral. People came to Jenny's in droves. It was very strange and very profitable, yet incredibly unfulfilling. In fact, the crowds drove us out of town, to Maine, where an invitation lay open.

thirteen

When I grow up, I want to be Stuart.

He was one of those guys from New York with hard Ss. I said, "becuzz"; he said, "bekos." He had a narrow face with a lot of facial hair and a nose that held up John Lennon glasses that I myself could never wear because my head was too big. I'd also require a pushpin between my eyes to keep them up. The lenses that manage to fit me are regularly smeared with cheek oil. He was slim, I wasn't. Even his mostly capped teeth were perfect. I guess that was the point.

I coveted those glasses. I even wished I was bald like Stuart was. My own teeth were, well, perfect, but there were moments when I wished I had caps the way I used to wish I had the peanut-butter-and-jelly sandwiches on Wonder Bread like the navy brats did, instead of my boxed lunch of rice, barbecued meat, vegetables, and ripe mango.

In New York, most recently in Chelsea, where he and Francesca owned a three-family brownstone, Stuart lived the artist's life. He designed things for illustrious, curiously anonymous projects, while managing their tenants and the ones in a building next door, which was owned by an elderly couple. He and Francesca adopted street dogs and turned them into perfect pets. I could barely get ours to heel, even with doggie therapy tapes from a big member subscription to our local PBS station.

For a time, Stuart lived in a loft in Hell's Kitchen, where he and Francesca roughed it during their early days. I found their history to be unspeakably cool, even as a kid from Guam who had gone from government cheese to Camembert—a success by any reckoning.

"You know, Dan," Jenny said brightly. "Francesca and Stuart didn't have *any* walls in that loft. Think about that."

Jenny had secretly asked David Rose, the psychiatrist, for a prescription narcotic so she could drag me on the plane to Maine. It was mildly successful. I was calm and happy throughout the four hours the plane sat on the runway. It was the last ninety minutes in the air to the Portland Jetport that were, to say the least, shaky. I stuttered to a woman across the aisle, "At l-l-least when c-c-cars c-c-crash, three hundred and f-f-fifty-seven people don't g-g-go down in a f-f-fireball."

But I was OK now. I was grateful to be on the ground, especially in Francesca and Stuart's presence.

"Didn't you guys have dry-cleaning bags up between the kitchen and bathroom?" Jenny asked.

"Practically!" Francesca said.

"It was viscose," Stuart said authoritatively.

He'd gone to design school. Francesca had graduated from college with a degree in French literature. She and Jenny had been friends since the early eighties, when Francesca wrote the menus for a dining room where Jenny was pastry chef. They hung out with Samantha, an earth mother sort who now lived in New Mexico making pottery and earrings, and pursuing a long-put-off degree in sculpture.

About a year before I rollicked like a half-nude Botero, foam in mouth, Francesca and Stuart sold their brownstone and the neighboring one—it had been bequeathed to them by the old couple. Francesca promptly quit her job as an editor of a major publishing house, and they moved to Maine, under a roof that cool dude Stuart designed himself.

"Francesca," Jenny said. "Your house looks great!"

Francesca smiled widely. She stretched her arms out and said, "I DEEEE-SERVE IT!"

The fact that the house was only fifty percent completed couldn't hide that it was a serious design effort. Stuart had done a good job.

Amid twenty acres on the island of Phippsburg in Midcoast Maine, the house was built in a clearing at the end of a secluded and heavily wooded driveway. As you approached it, the impulse might be to call it a modern take on the traditional New England saltbox, but. . .

Modern materials were expertly combined with traditional. Instead of granite foundations, Stuart had utilized split-faced concrete block, using granite, instead, for windowsills. A simple neoclassical effort, a portico with an especially austere pair of white columns covered the front door. On closer inspection, its decking proved to be not the usual pressure-treated pine. Instead, it was a three-inch mahogany luane which looks like suede.

The exterior siding was a cedar stained inky black-blue. Galvanized standing-seam roofing naturalized its appearance, animating the shiny mica-and-feldspar driveway and flecks of the mighty Kennebec River sparkling through the trees. As the raven flies, it must have looked like a rock riding on a glacier.

On the property was a large wood shed. Parked next to it was an old Chevy truck with a retro yellowed snowplow. An arachnoid tractor of noble provenance cut a handsome profile against the quiet forest. Throughout were trails along seventeenth century stone walls, most rolling toward the river. At the shore was a head light previously run by the U.S. Coast Guard. Francesca and Stuart had obtained its ownership for free by establishing a not-for-profit organization, increasing their shoreline by approximately two hundred feet. The headlight sat on an impressive crib of granite blocks rising from the cold, sturgeon depths and connected to the shore with a picturesque footbridge that lassoed across a marsh.

The interior was not finished. Judging by the exposed chimney of the same split-faced concrete block, discreet gray-painted cabinets topped with firestone (the manufactured soapstone-like surface Baby Boomers will remember from chemistry class), and the salvaged unmatched porcelain bathroom fixtures leaning in the unfinished, taped drywall halls, it was on its way to a quiet sort of greatness. The only hint of crap was an ominous second structure, larger than the house itself.

"It's Stuart's studio," Francesca reported through admirable caps of her own.

I wished I knew them better, and they me; I hadn't spent much time with F&S. Once, Francesca had met us for a day in Boston when I dragged Jenny to the Flower Show to take a look at a new disease-resistant creeping rose I needed two hundred feet of. Other than harmlessly eavesdropping on the wives' phone conversations and reading their annual holiday cards, I barely knew them.

I can't explain why I was rendered speechless in their presence. "It's a gwate howpse," I garbled, finishing my drink.

Francesca took out years-old pictures of them in New York and Chicago. They looked so carefree at twenty-five, -six, and -seven in the big city. I thought to myself, Shit, I was living like a sixty-year-old in my twenties. Their icons were rock stars and Aldous Huxley, their must-haves Volkswagen cars and big hair. Such pressure. The icons of my midtwenties were houses, caponata, and halogen lighting. They were chasing concert T-shirts without condoms. I was Web surfing for copper screening in stinky clogs and chef's pants. Theirs was a simple time of Julia Child, Pears soap, wainscot, and a young, pudgy Bob Vila. Mine was of the overblown adoration of Parmesan, bath-and-body conglomerates, and the cult of house and garden.

Thankfully, Stuart and I had something to talk about. He was in the middle of his own attempt to keep up with house gorgeous and was extremely inquisitive about my own "processes" of house ownership. He offered me a refill.

"Schpure!" I said happily.

"I was really inspired to build our own place up here when you sent the videotape Christmas-card house tour," he said.

"Bweally?" I said gratefully. I could have peed on myself.

"Yeah, I admired those transoms above your French doors."

"Oh, well," I replied shakily, "actually, I'm kind of over them."

"What do you mean?" he said.

"Oh, we've changed it completely—not the building itself, just the crap. Too much work," I said.

"Now, Dan, don't make it sound like we're minimalists," Jenny insisted.

"It's not like we're bninminimalists," I said apologetically.

"Minimalism isn't as simple as being spare," Stuart said with slow suspicion.

I knew that. I remembered that from college.

Immediately, something inside me, or inside Stuart, signaled me to stop talking. I felt like I didn't know what I was talking about and I became hot and embarrassed. In their midst it didn't matter that at my restaurant back home, Academy Award nominees were regulars.

"Do you know much about the minimalist movement, Dan?" Stuart asked.

"No, I don't actually," I said, trying to be cavalier.

"Be careful," he said. "You don't know who you might seat at that fancy restaurant of yours."

"You mean the one in Harbor Country?" I played the bon vivant.

"Oh! You have a nice restaurant!" Francesca called from the couch where she sat alongside Jenny.

"I know it's nice," I said meekly.

"Stanley Tigerman lives there, you know," she said.

"Sure, he does," Jenny said.

"So?" I said.

"He comes to Jenny's," Jenny said.

"I've never met him personally," I said, "but I've seen his name on the resos a lot."

Francesca smiled broadly and shrugged her shoulders at Stuart. She repeated how happy she was that we were there and spent the rest of the evening sharing secret signals with her husband, my hero.

In bed I asked Jenny why I had to know who Stanley Tigerman was. "He's the famous Chicago architect, Dan; you know, the one who has a house in Lakeside," she said.

"You mean the small metal one. I've heard people talk about it. And that he's famous," I said.

"OK, now you know. Good night." She rolled over and pulled the sheets over her shoulders.

Well, I always knew, I thought to myself. People in Harbor Country thought it was a shitty little house and couldn't get over what all the fuss was about. Who'd spend good money for that?

I was to embarrass myself a few more times in the presence of the great F&S, mostly by not connecting quickly to Stuart's avant-garde notions. Mercifully, they worked and when they did, Jen and I ventured beyond Phippsburg.

We found ourselves on Georgetown Island, which jutted out into the Atlantic and was inhabited primarily by lobster fishermen and year-round locals. At the southern tip, the Georgetown Lobster Pound served haddock sandwiches and deep-fried clams. It became an instant favorite haunt. As often as we could, Jen and I would secretly high-tail it to our newfound island to revisit ocean views and the heady smell of deep-fried New England cooking.

One day we explored a road that was cut out of the woods. Mosquitoes exploded onto the windshield, and fine dust came through the air vents. I wanted to back out but Jenny urged me to continue. After about two more minutes the woods opened up to a vista—a secluded bay. The road narrowed and veered right. On the bay side were unremarkable, if not run-down, camp houses. A lone power line indicated that there was probably nothing else to see had we continued, but we did so anyway. After a few hundred feet the road stopped. We got out and walked to where the land slid into the water. An old boathouse melted into the shore.

"Look," I said, "it's in the water."

"Sheesh," Jenny replied.

We knew, being from a waterfront community ourselves, that the EPA and municipal sorts didn't allow in-water structures anymore. This was a sight, indeed.

Dodging mosquitoes, we ran back to the car. On our way out, we noticed an old for sale sign, as decrepit as the boathouse, hidden in the brush. A while later at a supermarket in town, we poked through some real estate listings. There were three properties listed for sale in Georgetown. None of them were where we had been.

Jenny smiled. "Only if we sell the restaurant—"

"Which we're not going to do," I responded quickly.

We walked into a real estate office anyway to casually ask about it. "It's been for sale for years, but we took it off a couple of years ago," the real estate agent told us. "There's a problem with the easement. The neighbors get to use the driveway and nobody wants their neighbors driving through their property and parking in front of their house."

That fixed that. Jenny left our information with the agent so we could get mailings of their brochures.

Later, we told our hosts how we had spent our day.

I was surprised to find out that Stuart and Francesca actually looked down on Georgetown because its government was less strict than Phippsburg's. Apparently, Georgetown allowed new homes to be constructed on properties as small as one acre. In Phippsburg, the minimum was five acres. To F&S, this marred Georgetown's cachet, and Maine in general. They both, as it turned out, served in local Phippsburg government.

"That many people deplete well water," Stuart said.

Then he and Francesca then fired off a blinding succession of opinions.

"Can you imagine the septic runoff?"

"Why would you want neighbors as close as one acre?"

"I don't want to see anybody!"

"If your neighbor is a lobsterman, forget it."

"Messy yards, no way, José."

"One day I saw someone standing at the driveway. I had to ask them what they were doing there," Francesca revealed wildly. "Stuart wasn't home."

Stuart looked at Francesca. "When was that?" he asked, surprised.

"Two months ago," she said. "Different from when we saw someone standing there. Someone else was at the end of our driveway, standing there."

"See?" Stuart said, looking at Jenny and me.

"I think he was looking at the driveway salt," Francesca whispered, indicating the intent to thieve.

"You guys aren't thinking of buying in Georgetown, are you?" Stuart said.

"Well...,"Jenny said.

"Obviously, not any time soon," I chuckled. "We've got plenty of house and work in Michigan."

"One day," Jenny said lightly.

"One day you'll buy in Phippsburg," Francesca declared. "And Stuart can design your house!"

"On a small lot," I quickly insisted before I remembered that Stuart scared me. I shrank. "If possible; you know what I mean."

"Hmpf," he grunted.

By the time an excruciatingly slow piece of barbed wire called dinner pulled itself out of my ass, I was ravenous. We all were. Jenny grilled chicken with blanched garlic and fresh rosemary under the skin. As I had since I was a poor kid growing up on Guam, I crunched the bones and dug out the kidneys. Black friends in college had noted that I ate chicken like a brother. Francesca and Jenny were going at it, too, like sisters. The women and I tore into dinner with equal verve. Except, of course, that Stuart watched me all the while.

"I've never been that hungry," he muttered in a low voice.

"Oh, Stuart," Francesca said.

Out of the corner of my eye I saw her silently indicate to Stuart to stop. Then I heard them whisper something.

"Huh?" I said.

It dawned on me that I was probably disgusting him. Embarrassed, I stopped eating, wiped my mouth, and asked Stuart what was inside his large studio.

"I take it you haven't met Stanley Tigerman," he said bringing a perfectly dissected piece of boneless, skinless chicken breast to his skinny red lips.

RESCUE RELATIONSHIPS
TRUE FRIEND TEST

Q: HOW DO YOU KNOW IF YOUR FRIENDS LIKE YOU LESS THAN THEIR HOUSE?

A. *You have to leave your dogs at home.*

B. *They follow you around with coasters.*

C. *They never serve barbecued ribs or corn on the cob inside the house.*

D. *They make you help them cook in their fabulous kitchen.*

E. *All of the above.*

F. *Just D.*

STEP 3: IMPROVE

REINTEGRATION • *n.* *1 the process of reestablishing reality following the First Edit. **2** an attempt at normality subsequent to a comprehensive removal of crap **3** the point at which original style emerges **4** prolonged rectification of the cluttered home*

fourteen

We were back from Maine about a month when it hit me: Change sucks a moose's anus.

I stood before the Holding Area (previously known as my garage), surveying the few chosen items that would survive Rescue Step III. I thought about my seizure and depression, and how they led to this moment. Then my mind raced, wondering if I had heard correctly what Stuart whispered to Francesca. *Tiresome idiot?* I boosted myself with thoughts of my entrepreneurial triumphs, conquering sleepless nights and heartache over things like *Am I going to make payroll? Is the bank going to approve our commercial mortgage? Is the bullshit town of Lakeside really going to turn down the transfer of our liquor license?*

The liquor license matter, in particular, was a problem that loomed constantly during the early days of the restaurant. It was a serious threat to our livelihood. In Harbor Country there was always a group of influential townies who felt they owned Lake Michigan and were ready to picket the state government, demanding that it decline our transfer request every step of the way. Jenny and I actually transferred the license twice, once to the old leased site and most recently to the new. Oh, and God! Were the public hearings ugly. We were going to ruin property values, they screamed. We'd attract the wrong kind of people to the lake. Sixty-year-olds stepped up to the microphone at public meetings to ask what they would tell their children about crime when they grew up.

The legal expenses were ridiculous. People were unkind. Between all that and having the entire town turn on us during the holidays, telling me how fucked up we were if they waited ten minutes for their table, I thought there was a lot to resent Harbor Country for, most especially the stupid peer pressure I buckled under in the house-proud game.

When I cull through all this junk, I said to myself, we are gonna have one hell of a garage sale, and all the prices are going to be really high. All of Harbor Country will come because the sign on the mailbox out front will read Tag Sale, so that will make them start drooling. They'll buy all this crap up and crap up their houses.

But there were miles to go before I could sleep.

It is time for you to meet the New Pantry.

RESCUE ESSENTIAL
THE NEW PANTRY

The New Pantry is a space, usually a closet or small room, where cookery, nonfood products, appliances of infrequent use, and tools of frequent use are organized for ease of access and inventory.

Don't get your old pantry in a wad. The New Pantry is actually a hybrid of the old butler's pantry and a storage system that has long been employed by large hotels. This system is usually a large "cage" somewhere in a hotel's bowels filled with items needed for special occasions and events that crop up every now and then. It holds things like extra dishes; the odd, huge stockpot; extra chairs; cleaning materials; lightbulbs; and tools. In fact, these cages sometimes contain a washer and dryer just in case the dining-room captain spills a sticky sauce béarnaise upon his cuff, or the linen service falls through. And they do. (Recall the reason I ran into Alexandria O'Malley at Mariah Sook's Dry Cleaners in Michigan City.)

This cage holds all the things that need to be handy for the particular hotel's culture but cannot get in the way of conducting day-to-day business. Storing these extras somewhere other than the kitchen, bathrooms, laundry, and dining rooms allows for employees to work solely on the tasks at hand.

It spares everyone horrendous clutter, leaving the storing and inventorying of what is periodically necessary to a manager.

At the conclusion of Step II, you've got Grandmother's pasta machine in the Holding Area handed to you at her deathbed and which you only use for Italian Christmas. It doesn't belong with everyday traffic in your newly Rescued kitchen. But it is a part of your life. It belongs in the New Pantry (not back in the cabinet you took it from).

You have Granddad's lobster pot that you use every Fourth of July that was previously stored in the corner cabinet. That's where it would fit, right? The cabinet, by the way, was originally designed for cutting boards, which were put somewhere else, gathering dust. Put the lobster pot in the New Pantry. There's more to follow, but you get the idea.

Step III of the Rescue is REINTEGRATION. A way of thinking that IMPROVES the way you interact with your things.

Before you start hauling things from the Holding Area back into the house, let's address items that we hadn't bothered with during the First Edit. Things in the proverbial junk drawer, food items, cleaning supplies, storage bags, foil, and plastic wrap. Here's what you do:

MARRY LIKE SUBSTANCES AND PRODUCTS

Take all the duplicates of food items in your cupboards that are half-empty and marry them. Don't just marry once, either. Marry often.

Here's a big thing at my house: tea bags. We've got boxes and boxes of tea bags that are half-empty. Get rid of the boxes and combine the tea bags. Don't worry about mixing them up. The individual bags are marked and have distinct smells. Do the same thing for separate bags of flour, sugar, chocolate chips, walnuts, etc. Dry grocery is pretty much a no-brainer.

Wet grocery products need a little more thought. For example, if you have both imitation vanilla extract and pure vanilla extract, you can do a couple of things. You can get rid of the cheap stuff or you can marry them. I know, I know. I can just hear the screams of the food editors at Gourmet magazine (mea fucking culpa), but you know what? Who gives a shit! They're not picking up your dry cleaning. Unless you're making crème brûlée for the James Beard Crème Brûlée Extravaganza, chances are your friends or kids aren't going to detect the vanilla scandal in their

Toll House cookie. To be honest, neither will the judges at the contest; they're more interested in the custard's texture. Plus they eat way too much and their kidneys are probably shot. This affects taste.

The same goes for oils if you find that you're stuck with jar after jar of raffia-adorned herb-infused olive oils. With the exception of truffle oil, go ahead and combine half-empty jars and just use them up. Garlic oil mixed with rosemary oil will taste better than the individual concoctions. If you really like those wacky hot pepper oils, then mix them up, too. The goal is to have one jar of one type of oil instead of several irrelevant subtypes. Do the same for vinegars, soy sauces, barbecue sauces, hot sauces, etc.

As you're dealing with these things, your impulse might be, "Oh, I could use those bubbly green jars from Pier 1 Imports that I have sitting in the Holding Area."

Well, yes, you could. But you must fight that urge and only use the bottles the products came in. Falling into the "recontainering" loop will cause a relapse. Before you know it, there will be cute container after cute container and then all of a sudden you'll be taking ten steps for a teaspoon of sugar for your coffee. Fuck that shit.

Nonfood items like Ziplock bags and garbage bags benefit from a good, easy marriage, too. Chemical products, however, require a bit more attention.

NEVER, EVER MIX CHEMICALS THAT ARE NOT THE SAME BRAND

Clorox bleach goes with Clorox bleach. Ajax goes with Ajax, not Comet. Some might say, *Oh, but Comet is the same as Ajax.* Not true. They might have the same purpose, but they have different ingredient combinations. Do not second-guess the chemistry or the potential danger of mixing. Just don't go there. While our goal is to create a state of organization with seemingly perilous bravado, we must preserve our good health.

By the end of Step III, the only cleaning products that should remain under your sink are some kind of sink cleaner, dishwashing soap, and paper towels. The rest will be stored in the New Pantry in a spot you designate for cleaning products.

KEEP THINGS IN THEIR PACKAGING

For God's sake—enough of the recontainering in your kitchen. Your spaghetti doesn't need to go in the tall green glass container with the cute cork top. The box it came in is far and away technologically superior to anything

Smith & Hawken finds in Indonesia. The spaghetti, after all, survived being shipped across the country, if not overseas. Engineers were paid untold sums to make sure that little box could overcome humidity, pissed-off forklift operators, and overworked supermarket stockers. That's why the noodles come to you in such perfect shape. Simply placing them in your cupboard in their box is like early retirement for pasta. Get rid of the jar, put the spaghetti in the cupboard, and keep your life uncluttered.

Are you ready for more?

At this point, your kitchen is clean and free of clutter and extraneous dishes, pots, and accessories. Your food is organized and your surfaces gleam with the exception of a toaster and microwave, perhaps a Cuisinart or KitchenAid mixer, and an electric coffee pot. But it really isn't the set that your film needs for, say, the Thanksgiving scene.

And what about Thanksgiving? Are you going to have to throw away or sell Grandmother's turkey soup tureen?

Of course not.

My goal is not to pare your possessions down to the point where your personal history is desecrated. One of the objectives is to make the rooms in your house places where everyday enjoyment doesn't include setting up for relaxation and ease. Your new kitchen proper is where the everyday is celebrated. The New Pantry, therefore, is where the sometimes is stored.

RESCUE REITERATION
THE NEW PANTRY

The New Pantry is where you reintegrate only the most important possessions that are in your Holding Area back into your life but out of your way. It is separate storage for what you don't need most of the time.

A simple enough notion, but one that is so easily lost. Here's why:

You would think that a million cabinets would solve the problem of clutter, right? But what usually happens is that all the pots are grouped together in front of the two pans that you use seventy-five percent of the time. The three pots you use twenty-three percent of the time are somewhere behind a Dutch oven and double boiler that you never use. Are you following me? Cabinets, whether they are teak or cardboard, are designed for maximum storage, not your lifestyle. Even the Sultan of Brunei doesn't have kitchen cabinets that suit his lifestyle. He has servants. If you're overwhelmed it's because you're dealing on a daily basis with things that you only use two-percent of the time, if at all.

The New Pantry is where the rarely used pots need to go, unless you go completely minimalist and get rid of them. (Don't quote me on that minimalist bit, though.) But we're just normal working people. They need to be out of sight, out of mind, mercifully stored away from your field of vision so that your brain doesn't process clutter, but your heart and self-worth are satisfied with a sense of possession. In other words, you can still brag about your Calphalon. You just don't have to get your panties in a wad about the dust it collects in that UFO pot rack.

ESTABLISHING THE NEW PANTRY

Obviously, you need a place for your New Pantry. If you have an old pantry, why not put it there? If you have a room that is now empty as a result of your First Edit, consider it.

The New Pantry has less to do with the space and more to do with the idea and a new set of habits. It's a new way to THINK about storing.

WHAT, NO FOOD IN THE NEW PANTRY?

You'll notice that I haven't thus far mentioned food as part of the New Pantry. That's because there isn't supposed to be any food stored there. Food should be stored in the kitchen, in cabinets above the counters, where it's within easy reach, in cabinets that once housed your redundant collection of cookware and plates.

In our house, we used the pantry almost exclusively for food. However, it was relatively far from the counter/work space and food was out of easy (arm's length) reach. Why walk to get an ingredient when you're cooking? Reach for it instead.

Americans tend to hoard foodstuffs partly because bulk shopping has swept the land. The New Pantry does not support this kind of accumulation. Marrying food items and putting them into the limited cabinet spaces (as opposed to large pantries) encourages more thoughtful marketing and cooking.

Now think about that for a minute: small amounts of food into small spaces.

This doesn't mean that you'll go to the store more often. How many people do you know who go to Sam's Club really only shop just once a month? It doesn't happen.

What I'm proposing is that you go to the store on a regular basis and buy less. You buy five pounds of flour rather than ten. You buy one ounce of oregano rather than a 4 oz bag. It's a new-again way of marketing, one that allows you to buy what you really eat and use.

Instead of storing bulk foods; you're simply replacing regularly consumed items.

More important, when you go to the market to pick up your things you won't be loaded down with extra stuff you bring home to inventory at unneeded expense. The supermarket has the space, staff, and budget—let them keep it! Just take home what you need between trips.

I'd like to think that if your kitchen is set up this way you'll be encouraged to smell the damn roses. Observe the life that's going on around you. Life that you've missed on your mad dash to and from the wholesale club to get that lifetime supply of milk chocolate chips put away. Where do people store those washing machine-sized packs of toilet paper anyway?

I know what you're thinking: Toilet paper is cheaper when you buy one hundred rolls. I agree. A less cluttered life, however, is more precious than the cents you save.

The New Pantry is a tool for your IMPROVED way of thinking. Keep envisioning that cage in the basement of grand hotels as we rethink the following rooms.

BATHROOMS RETHOUGHT

There are really only three things you do in the bathroom, if you will, the essential Ss. Shaving, Showering, and S-nevermind. That's it.

The basic tools of the room, therefore, are a sink, a shower/tub, and a toilet. Bidets if you are so inclined or have drunk Peter Mayle's Kool-Aid. Bathrooms are not about getting dressed. They're not about storing toiletries. They're not even about putting on your makeup—I can't tell you how many times Jenny's dropped her makeup in the toilet. That should tell you something. And—big "and"—bath rooms are certainly not about remembering the spirit.

Don't get me wrong—if you have an epiphany in there, more power to you. Miracles, however, being the heavenly doves they are, tend to be capricious about where they flutter. It's utter nonsense to construct, contrive, or design a bathroom with philosophies beyond physiology. Screw this temple spa bullshit. I mean, really, how perverse can you get? The toilet in Michigan had a view of my collection of pagoda dogwoods. Why? I don't know. All I ever looked at was the Star, between looking for skin-cancer lesions and breast lumps during that little depression of mine.

The bathroom, however, doesn't need to be something that looks like a hospital lavatory. It does, actually, benefit from a bit of the designer's touch: Use antique or framed mirrors instead of plain new ones. Upgrade the hardware. Replace the shower curtain with a glass door. Take down a shelf that once held perfume bottles and knickknacks and put in its place a nicely framed photo or painting. These all make a bathroom look nicer, but they don't add to the clutter.

Ever wonder how the bathroom became such a traffic jam anyway? Here's where I think we went wrong.

I've probably lived in eight places since I moved out of my mother's house, mostly apartments and houses that (until Michigan) were built either at the turn of the century or within the last twenty years. The bathrooms in the older houses and apartments seemed generally to lack a vanity. At some point in the last century, I'll venture to say during the last half, the bathroom became a place to store.

I'm guessing that you grew up in this "store-it-in-the-bathroom" era and, therefore, have done your share of waiting to get into it. Imagine how much time could have been saved over all those years if we hadn't been crossing our legs waiting for our sisters to put on mascara while the toilets went unused. I'm fairly sure that the incidence of third and fourth bathrooms in single-family homes would be significantly less frequent if the slightest consideration was made before we jumped on the design bandwagon. Health & Beauty works well for retailing, but it doesn't make sense in a Rescued home. Peeing is one thing. Flat ironing your mane is quite another.

Activities other than the Three Ss have become bad habits we've relegated to the bathroom. To cope with the anxiety of having to wait to relieve ourselves, we've learned to simply get bigger or build more bathrooms because we think that's the obvious solution. We haven't stopped to think that bigger bathrooms with more storage aren't saving us any more time. They're just costing us money.

If you don't believe me, consider the famous double sink. "Oh, we put in that double sink so I don't have to wait for Sarah to do her thing while I do my thing."

Oh yeah? What happens to Sarah when you need to take a dump? You and her lip lining won't be occuring in the same place at the same time.

Do you see the pattern? Big bathroom with lots of storage, still no time. Still in a hurry. Still overwhelmed.

We have to return to the basics in the bathroom, which means taking out the mousse, the makeup, the hair dryer—the finishing touches of getting dressed. As well, we need to remove the cleaning products, prescription drugs, the little bottles of hotel shampoo, and the thirty-three-gallon bag of cotton balls from Wal-Mart.

PRESCRIPTION DRUGS

Again, never, ever put your prescription drugs in any bathroom, or for that matter, in the New Pantry, if they are public spaces.

First of all, we all snoop in medicine cabinets. (How else would I know that House took Rogaine?) It is no one's business what your doctor prescribes for you. Additionally, they are controlled substances. If you have teenagers, children, and visitors about, you obviously can't police them while they're using a bathroom. You have significantly more control over your private space, like your bedroom. Keep prescription drugs by your bed, either in your nightstand or on a table.

HAIR DRYER, MAKEUP, MOISTURIZERS

Placing hair dryers near a sink is an idiotic endeavor. Just don't do it. Hair dryers and these other items belong in an area outside the bathroom that you designate as a dressing area. It can be the surface of a chest of drawers or a dedicated space in your closet. I think another reason most people insist on keeping these items in bathrooms is lighting. Typically, lighting around a mirror or above a sink is good for these tasks. Simply put a mirror and a light near the chest of drawers I just mentioned. Like prescription drugs, they really need to be in a controlled area free from as much public access as possible.

EXTRA SOAPS, SHAMPOOS, BAND-AIDS, TOILET PAPER

If you're overwhelmed, I bet you have a lot of extra soap from hotels. It's just the way it is. I think we accumulate these extras, determined that we won't be caught without. Instead, we end up wasting a lot of energy navigating around the loot. Collect them for placement in the New Pantry in a section you designate for health and beauty, such as extra bottles of aspirin, extra dental floss and toothbrushes, and duplicates of lip balm.

Part of the New Pantry, therefore, will end up being sort of a mini-drugstore. You'll be amazed at how many duplicates of these types of things will end up in your Holding Area. Gather them up, inventory them like your own private Rite Aid, and enjoy how much money you don't have to spend for a while.

CLEANING PRODUCTS

If you outfitted your home as we did in Michigan, you have a bottle of Windex, Soft Scrub or Ajax for the sink and toilet, Tilex or Comet Bathroom Cleaner for the shower, and a role of paper towels under the sink in every bathroom. Bad idea. Waste of money. They belong in the New Pantry in a section you will designate just for cleaning products.

In time, you'll never again make duplicate purchases of cleaning products. One look in one spot will tell you what's missing. When you scrub the four sinks throughout your house, you will use the same can of Comet until it runs out. Otherwise the one can under each sink crystallizes before it gets used and you throw it, money, and time out.

THE LAUNDRY ROOM RETHOUGHT

What is it about laundry rooms and the garbage they attract? In our laundry room, whatever we took out of the dryer to hang up on the pole stayed there. Whatever stray sock or ruined T-shirt I kept (in case I wanted to paint frescoes) stayed there. Whatever tool I'd bring up from the basement always ended up staying in the laundry room. And, of course, there was that thing the size of a donated-organ cooler made from used-up Bounce dryer sheets and lint. It just stayed there. Why?

Earlier I said that being overwhelmed was actually a luxury. We can afford to make a space exclusively for washing clothes; therefore, we can afford to leave things hanging around the place and the anxiety that follows. Ever consider that there is no dirty dish room or dirty floor room?

Laundry rooms are not self-cleaning. They cannot be a repository for clothes that won't fit in your wardrobe. Nor can they be the room where stray cleaning products, wrenches and screwdrivers taken out of their sets, and vacuum-cleaner bags luxuriate. Only soap, bleach, fabric softener, spray starch, Woolite, an iron, and an ironing board are allowed to live there. Everything else goes into the New Pantry, or the garbage.

TOOLS RETHOUGHT

There are always tools we use more often than others: a power drill, a hammer, pliers, a small level. They need to be handy. I recommend they be put in the New Pantry in a specially designated area. On the other hand, table saws, drill presses, power sanders, and the like belong in the basement if you're a handy person who uses them regularly. If you aren't, why do you own these tools? Do you think you're going to find the time to build a Nordic warship in the next five years?

I have a good friend who has all the tools in his basement but can't build a dining table until he spends thirty thousand dollars building a garage/workshop. I want to have him exorcised. Forget about it. You work hard. You have no time. Good wood is expensive. Sell the tools, go out and buy a nice table (up to thirty thousand dollars if you've got it to throw around), and eat.

So do you get the New Pantry? It is exactly like those cages in the basements of great hotels, except it's not in your dungeon. It's your supply depot—a room in which to keep all the supplies and tools you use to live your regular life, but out of your everyday way.

The model on which most of our homes are based has storage scattered throughout the house by category, meaning crap is side by side, and in front of, the few things you use on a regular basis. This means you are constantly juggling the bulk of your possessions to get to your simple, everyday needs.

Stop it!

I'm not telling you to get rid of all of it. I'm telling you to get it out of your way so it doesn't bog you down. Throw the shit in the New Pantry.

fifteen

By April, the house was crapless, and I secretly wished we hadn't actually built it. We could have sliced off two thousand square feet, kept only the deep end of the pool, divided the property, and sold off the parterre to a nice homosexual couple who'd turn it into the Taj Mahal. Oh, well. At least the house wasn't worthless; it retained the money we put into it. But I could have saved myself years of pain by simply putting that money in the bank.

Let's not dwell on it, because now I've got new attitude and a new room.

RESCUE ESSENTIAL
THE NEW WALK-IN

A closet or room exclusively dedicated to the storage of off-season outerwear and outerwear accessories, bags and luggage, and heavy boots and shoes.

In other words, the New Walk-In relieves your regular closet of the burden of storing weatherproof clothing and accessories. It allows your regular closets to be put to maximum storage use for clothes that are your primary and secondary layers. Every raincoat, three-season blazer, down vest and fleece sweatshirt should go into the New Walk-In. All bags, purses, luggage, and backpacks should also go in the New Walk-in. A good question to ask yourself: Is it an outer layer that repels water and cold? If the answer is yes, then it doesn't belong in your regular closet.

Like the New Pantry, this, too, is a "cage" for your clothes and accessories. Take the stuff you don't wear ninety percent of the time (which we all know is ninety percent of the clothes in your closet) and place it all in the New Walk-In.

When you begin to use the New Walk-In, your regular closets and armoires become self-organizing and spacious. Please don't take this opportunity to go out and buy more clothes, or get sloppy again. This is the perfect time to create and reinforce strict rules about how you store your first- and second-layer garments.

CLOTHES RETHOUGHT

If you're like me, you regularly wear a fraction of the clothes you own. If this is your truth, you don't need to look any farther to demystify how to edit your clothes—you already know what you need.

When I edited my closet, it took me all of two hours. I already knew the items I wore over and over. We did laundry once a week, which meant I was hardly ever going through the "passive inventory" in my closet for something to wear. Instead, what I wore during the week moved from my back to the washer and dryer or dry cleaners' then into my closet (if I didn't just put them on). I simply looked in the hamper (which I got rid of later), figured out that it was four days until laundry duties, and made a mental note of the clothes I absolutely knew I would wear until laundry day. The rest went out, if not to Goodwill or the garbage, right into the New Walk-In.

It will be a shock when you realize how much money you have sitting in passive inventory versus how little is actually left in your closet. Over and above the money, think of all the time you spend picking out the clothes, trying them on, getting to stores, parking, dealing with traffic jams. All this for an item of clothing you haven't given a second thought to in months, maybe years. Get rid of it!

Jenny did not make quite so drastic a culling of her closet. And the truth is, it is none of my business what she wants to keep or throw out. Other people's clothing is personal and should, therefore, be off limits to the person in charge if it gets problematic. I don't ever want to suggest that you bulldoze your way into your housemates' most private spaces. It is enough to do that in the common areas.

KIDS' CLOTHES

Children are keen fashion observers. They will hardly miss discarded clothes because they are constantly wanting new looks and growing into new sizes. Know your kid's clothes fetishes before you Rescue their closets. Remember they are entitled to their private spaces, too.

But imagine getting rid of the piles in their bedrooms. No more plunging through the depths of the unwanted and discarded for that single shirt or pair of groovy socks. Doesn't that sound like nirvana? Can you smell the teen spirit? Young children are only interested in what they want to wear. They might actually get more interested in becoming involved with laundry if you cull as I suggest.

WAIT! So you've culled, tossed, and stored the outer garments in the New Walk-In. Don't think you're done. You aren't yet equipped with theory so that you don't find yourself in this position again. Here are the basics:

THE THREE RULES OF CRAPLESS CLOTHES OWNERSHIP

I. FOLD LIKE YOU WORK AT THE GAP

I used to tease Wes all the time about how he folded his clothes. In fact, I couldn't stand to be around him the same weekend he was doing laundry. Wes was a crease freak. He obsessed about stacking his T-shirts like they were in a Gap store.

I didn't give too much thought about stuffing T-shirts and socks into drawers until I set out to Rescue myself. My T-shirts never looked as sharp as Wes's even though they were just as clean. Matching socks took forever. Wes's method worked. A little work up-front saves time and aggravation.

So here I am, a convert.

Easily a good seventy-five percent of the clothes that made it through your First Edit can be folded, including clothes that have remained on hangers for more than one month. Here's why: Hanging is very hard on clothes and causes most garments to become misshapen. When I was going through my closet, I discovered shirts and jackets that I really liked and wanted to keep were ruined at the shoulders. Don't fool yourself into thinking that storing clothes on a hanger means you won't have to press them. Unless they are fresh from the cleaner's, chances are they've just been, well, hanging around. No doubt they'll need a serious pressing or laundering to realign the knit.

Does this mean you have to invest in dressers? Nope.

Assuming that you decide to fold most of your clothes, a significant amount of the hanging space in your closet will become free. Here you can set up shelves (either premade or custom built) to store the folded clothes. Place shorts with shorts, sweaters with sweaters, T-shirts with T-shirts. Keep the in-season clothes at the most convenient levels and then rotate according to seasons.

Shirts or blouses from the dry cleaner's should come "boxed," that is, folded and encased in a plastic sleeve ready for neat, wrinkle-free stacking. Dump the hanging bit.

2. KEEP CLOTHES ON A HANGER A MAXIMUM OF ONE MONTH

If you keep clothes on hangers that haven't been touched in one month, take them off and fold them. Even if they are winter-weight suits? Sure. Hanging for several summer months will twist them and they'll need a dry cleaning anyway when it cools down again. It doesn't matter if it's a gown or ski suit, if something is hanging that long, it isn't in peril of immediate use. It really should go into some kind of long-term storage.

Your closet is not long-term storage. One of the connotations of the word clothes is that you wear them. Clothes that aren't worn regularly move to the realm of "collection." Your closet is a place for your actively worn clothes. An old suit or a tea gown should be donated to a charity of your choice, sold, or properly boxed and moth-proofed. At least make an effort to preserve these items so you can pass them off to your kids, who will throw them away when you're dead or not looking.

3. GET RID OF THE HAMPER

Hampers are a way to forget about laundry. They are little chests designed to look pleasing and permanent. They make putting off the maintenance of your washable clothes acceptable, which it is absolutely not if we are going to Rescue ourselves.

Hampers allow us to develop bad cleaning habits, such as prioritizing dirt. Dirt is dirt. I know many people who only wash half their dirty clothes because they don't have enough colors to make a full load. Instead, they throw the few colors back into the hamper and then weeks go by while stains are busy setting and God knows what manner of vermin spawns. Don't do that. Any dirty laundry is good enough reason to run the washing machine.

So does that mean I wash the whites with the colors?

No, of course not. But it does mean that you can mix your jeans with your dish towels and socks. My mother used to have what she called her "jeans load" and I am sure that some people have towel loads and bath-mat loads. Listen, if it's white and cotton, it's white and cotton—wash that bath mat with your butt thongs, who cares?

Get rid of the hamper and place an old-fashioned laundry basket at a discreet corner of your room. When it looks full, it's ready for the wash. Don't worry about wasting water. There's plenty of it if you budget right. Worry instead that you're wasting your time getting stressed, which leads to far more wasteful habits. Rescue yourself and sign up for a walkathon to save our oceans.

LINENS

Linen closets are always full of towels, sheets, and pillowcases that never get used and grow smelly from mold and poor air circulation. You have better things to do than maintain yet another closet. Cull through your collection of sheets and towels, bring the ones you absolutely use into the respective bedrooms, and store them in the armoire or a dresser drawer. Get rid of the old ones. Give them away. Just don't make a fucking quilt.

Actually, what we know as the linen closet doesn't make sense in a newly edited space. If you have one now, consider using it for either the New Pantry or the New Walk-In. If you are building a house, scrap the linen closet.

"My God!" Wes exclaimed. "Your damn house has gone on Atkins! Honey, its hooge!"

"You know, that's exactly what my staff says behind my back," I said.

Jenny and I had invited Wes and Bill over for Easter Dinner, but only Wes came. "What did you do? I didn't think you could pull it off, personally," he said.

"Dan put together a house that now maintains us, Wes," Jenny said proudly, "not one that we maintain. He better not do it again."

"Well, it looks great. Honest," Wes said. "It's actually kind of nice to look at your house and not wonder what magazine I saw it in."

That meant a lot. He didn't just say that to anyone. We'd gotten his personal Stamp of Approval.

"What's next?"

"TAG SALE!" I said, laughing.

"Mother of God, there'll be a goddamned stampede!" he cackled.

We roared with more laughter. He offered a toast to my apparent success and to the belated year anniversary of my seizure. Then he dropped the bombshell. "We're breaking up," he said.

Jenny gasped. We'd been told that Bill wasn't coming because something had happened in Mexico, a manufacturing problem. "So he's not really in Mexico?" Jenny asked.

"Bill's in Mexico, all right" Wes replied. "She's keeping it."

The news blew us away. We'd grown up together in Harbor Country. The guys had been together seventeen years. They'd seemed happy—they were the happy poster boys for the Chicago Hamptons. I had to ask Wes the obvious question. Why?

He told us what Bill's reasons were, but he didn't have any of his own that he felt were good enough to end their marriage. He was shocked, and hurt. What else could we say? "I see you kept the chairs," he said sarcastically.

"You can have the damn chairs. . . .,"I said.

"Oh, Wes," Jenny cried. I was getting choked up myself.

"Nah," he said. "French bordello is so 1998."

sixteen

Jenny and I stole away to Maine twice more.

Back home in Michigan, I convinced myself that I had overdosed on DEET. I had smeared an unnatural amount of it on me as we walked the bay in Georgetown. Yankee Mosquitoes are as tough as bats. They don't exactly hold their pinkies out when they're sucking your blood, no matter how discreetly you sneak in to look at property.

I had barely recovered from my flight tranquilizer, and Jenny had just settled into the Jacuzzi when the real estate agent called.

"Can you hold on—for one minute?" I said groggily. "My wife should talk to you."

I called out to Jen to pick up the phone. A few minutes later I felt her wet hair dripping on my shoulder.

"So is that the realtor in Maine with an offer we won't be able to resist?" I asked, surrendering to the tranquilizer's lingering temptations.

"Yes, the realtor has an offer we can't resist," she said quietly.

"Well?" I slurped. "Is the price right?"

"It's in the ballpark."

A few seconds passed. "Do you want it?" I asked, slightly irritated.

"Hmm..."

"Anything else?"

"There are two offers, actually," she said, clearing her throat.

"Lemme see," I said lazily, "the twenty-eight acres to the left of Francesca and Stuart have a title problem, but it's fixable, and Stuart's friend is willing to divide his fifty acres so long as we promise to spit at the locals."

I bristled at the thought. I couldn't shake Stuart from my head. He'd gotten so bold about not really liking me. He whispered unkind things—even Jenny heard them. I rolled over. Jenny had a distant look.

"What?" I said.

"It's the realtor down the street," she said, detached. "There are offers to buy the house and the restaurant."

"What?!" I screamed, suddenly airborne.

I was so loud the dogs started barking and Jenny ran screaming to the toilet, where she peed, laughing. I spent the next couple of minutes bellowing, Get the fuck out! Get fucking off me!

Jenny and I had been, in fact, more proactive about moving to Maine sooner, but we had kept it secret; no one else knew. Restaurants are a bear to unload, especially one so attached to a chef. We had even discussed turning the house into a duplex to tap into the lucrative rental market for when we sold Jenny's, but that was it. Neither was even a remote possibility. Until now.

Who. . . why. . . what ever would make anyone think we were for sale? Immediately an image of Allen and Alexandria O'Malley finished off my insecticide-induced haze. Of course, they gabbed. In true Harbor Country style, the body wasn't cold before they started touring the house. But I didn't care.

I ran to Jenny. "How did this happen?" I shivered.

"I mentioned it to House," she confessed. "Are you upset?"

I considered it. It had to be the O'Malleys. "Same buyer?"

"No."

I thought about the restaurant first. "So, is it bona fide?"

Jenny nodded. "A friend of one of my ex-partners."

"And the house?"

"Cash deal"

"You wanna do it?"

"You think I want to listen to you bitch about dishwashers all my life?" she blurted happily.

When the math was done, it all seemed possible. I spent many weeks with lawyers and accountants hammering out the purchase agreement for the business and drafted a four-month schedule by which the business transfer would take place. I worried needlessly that the liquor-license issue would screw up the deal but was told by the township that the license wasn't going to be physically transferred, per se, title was simply going to change. This process precluded a melodramatic town meeting where 60-year-olds would get up and express concerns for the kind of free-drinking community their 1-year-olds were born into. Whew!

The purchase of the house went more smoothly. The new owners bought several items in the Holding Area. Jenny and I had no problems figuring out what to bring with us to Maine. The obvious problem was where the hell we were going to live, so we went twice more to New England.

Let me tell you: Amtrak was one way to make cross-country house searching a nightmare, even as a bright new millennium approached.

"Why did I let you talk me into this?" Jenny glared.

We'd been stuck for two hours in Rensselaer, New York, just two miles past the train station. The conductor would not let us out for fresh air.

"Oh, so you like me dry heaving in midair, making all the passengers nervous then?" I said incredulously. I'd overcome a lot, the newfound fear of flying not being one of the triumphs.

Two miserable days after the train took off from Michigan City, Jenny and I crawled to F&S's. Our clothes stuck to us like fruit roll-ups; my new underwear adhered to my sworn privates like aspic to pâté. F&S were beside themselves that we were moving there. Even Stuart seemed to warm up a bit, like a boxer to a new punching bag. What kind of Mainers would we become?

"Oh, you know, I'll probably get a job baking cookies somewhere," Jenny answered Francesca, who was delightedly curious to know how Jenny pictured life in Maine.

"What about you, Dan?" asked Francesca.

Stuart looked on.

"I want to write a screenplay and cookbook, in that order," I declared happily.

Francesca coughed. "Well that's bold, Dan," she said. Her mock encouragement froze into a plastic smile.

"OK," Stuart replied. He looked at Francesca, who remained stuck in smiley horror. "It took me twenty-four months to get a design construction job here, you know. Do you even cook? Now you want to write a cookbook?"

Jenny said, "Oh, he's a great c—"

"So are you going to build or buy?" Francesca interjected.

"Did you go to cooking school, Dan?" Stuart demanded, driving on with his maddening agenda.

"No," I said.

"Neither did I, Stuart," Jenny said.

He gave Jenny a wide smile. "Ah, but you can cook, my dear."

"You'll find the right thing," Francesca said in an attempt to sooth the hackles shooting straight up my back.

"What's to find?" I said loudly. "I'm going to write."

"Just make sure I design the house," Stuart said, full of affirmation.

"Of course," I said, fantasizing about Amtrak's stale, slow air.

The trip was fruitless, and a life next to Stuart was beginning to seem less idyllic than the status quo. But people on a house search, as you know, are crazy. We were determined to return and stay with the bastard as often as necessary until we found it.

Back in Michigan, Jenny spent the next few weeks working side by side with the restaurant's new owners, making sure that while she was still in the kitchen, the food came out with her definitive stamp. That went on as long as it could without the inevitable conflicts two chefs, one incoming and one outgoing, created. Eventually, she let go of the kitchen's creative proprietorship, working more with introducing the wine vendors to the new owners. They were, after all, paying dearly for an exclusive right to get screamed at on New Year's Eve by the supposed friends of Oprah's hired help. She made a tremendous effort to tell people around town that selling the restaurant was her idea, not mine.

I spent my last days at Jenny's visiting with old customers I had never gotten time to know for reasons ranging from apprehensive *(He's friends with that guy who called us fucked-up)* to bashful *(She knew the paramedic who saw me with my pants off)* to indifferent *(House and Garden)*.

The black flies in July were no less insidious than being picked apart by Stuart as I sat, once more, at his table eating chicken, which Jenny had prepared at Francesca's request.

Predictably, I reached for the carcass and tore off the back. As I did, one of the tender rounds of meat cradled in the hip socket, the oyster, fell onto the table. I picked it up and popped it in my mouth.

"Jesus, Dan, do you mind?" Stuart whined dramatically.

"What? Stuart, what's with you and the way I eat? Your people eat fish balls, mine eat cartilage. My teeth can handle it, you know."

I checked to see if Jenny minded that I'd taken a sideways jab at his caps. She did. What the hell, I thought, I might as well eat the pope's nose. So I ripped the ass off the chicken. Crunch.

Stuart dropped his fork. The pained ping made everyone stop and look up. He wiped his mouth slowly, and then, like they used to do on Dynasty, he gave me a look up and down better than Joan Collins had ever done.

"You're an alien," he said flatly, "bekos real people don't eat like that."

And that, as they say, was it.

Rather than sputtering some incoherent native babble, I took a deep breath and in quick time recalled a dinner I recently had had with one of my new friends/old customers. We had eaten gigantic lobsters that were pan-fried with fermented black beans. He very politely had asked me if I liked lobster tamale before digging into his lobster's head.

"Are you kidding?" I had said. "My meal begins where most end."

"Good!" Stanley Tigerman himself replied. "You should see what I do to a chicken."

We sucked our lobster heads, oblivious to the onlookers. Then Stanley said something profound.

"Dan," he said, "the very rich and the very poor have the exact same taste. Take food. Marrow on toast points. Fish eggs, to be sure. Lobster heads presently."

I looked at Stuart, wiped my mouth on Francesca's best Crate & Barrels, and adjusted my imaginary Dynasty shoulder pads. "You know what, ass-hole? We can't buy in Phippsburg because Stanley Tigerman hates nature." I blinked quickly, then added, "We bought the bay parcel in Georgetown."

I was betting that Stanley Tigerman having something to do with me would undo Stuart. It did.

"Stanley Tigerman!" shrieked Francesca. "Stuart!"

I looked at the wings on the platter between us and asked confidently, "Are you going to eat those?"

Jenny blushed and quickly offered an overly apologetic explanation. "Stanley loves to design small houses and he never gets to. He's crazy about Dan. They get together and talk about tropical diseases."

"We discuss minimalism," I declared loudly. "It really does mean no crap."

Stuart clenched his mouthful of piano keys and I allowed a smile to spread confidently across my greasy lips.

"You should see how Stanley eats chicken," I said, smacking.

seventeen

Two weeks before the movers came, Jen and I took a long look at what
was left in the Holding Area. What was all this stuff? Relics, mementos,
baby clothes, Jenny's grandmother's purses. We asked ourselves, are they
relevant to our lives? The answer was, sure they are. Were they adding to
our workload by simply sitting dusty in the basement? Yes. Were we going
to discard everything then? No and yes.

There were some expensive items (a lot, actually) that hadn't been taken
back into the house, such as a stationary bike and a NordicTrack. There sat
a very large and expensive drill press I had hauled from the basement. I had
used it to drill exactly five holes for a trellis I saw on The New Yankee Work-
shop. I hadn't thought about it in five years. Did I keep it? Hell, no. So what
do you do with this stuff?

You already know that tucking the crap into the corners it came from is
not acceptable. One of the things you have learned thus far is that you have
to respect your storage areas, as well as the items you store in them. You
cannot return a perfectly unused stationary bike to the basement simply because you can't bear the guilt of discarding it.

Stop telling yourself that storing unwanted stuff is the same as not
throwing away money. What difference does the money make anyway, especially at this point? You wasted the money a long time ago. The bike isn't
money. It's really just a big canceled check (and even they get destroyed after
four years).

If you can realize that everything in your Holding Area is completely nonessential, then you've realized something MAJOR. The reward is you've now defined a healthy relationship with your accoutrements. Having done so, you can now reintegrate some of them into your life, but here's the deal:

THE SEVEN RESCUE RULES FOR INTEGRATING NONESSENTIALS

1. CHANGE HOW YOU INTERACT WITH THE NONESSENTIALS.

Try and find ways to make these things a part of your everyday experience. Take yearbooks out of dusty graves and place them proudly on your bookshelf; they deserve to be there as much as Ansel Adams does. Think of ways report cards and old schoolwork and essays can be incorporated with your school pictures in an album or photo box, but do so without running to the glue gun or emulating some craft project on TV or in magazines. Simply put them together. Jenny decided to keep her grandmother's memory alive day to day by using her vintage table linens and tossing out impersonal Williams-Sonoma ones. She didn't make some bullshit memory "art" to hang on the wall.

2. STORE "MUST KEEP" NONESSENTIALS OFF-SITE.

Who knows why you absolutely have to keep something that you've already determined has no use in your everyday life? Just know that you are allowed to. Junk like this makes us human. I couldn't get rid of an old sign that reads Open for Breakfast. We also have good one-of-a-kind rugs that appear to be the vague beginnings of a collection. We didn't quite yet know where they were going, but at the same time we didn't feel compelled to leave them behind. These things I put to the side so when the movers came, they would be tagged to go into storage (instead of being delivered to our house). In Maine, thirty dollars a month pays for climate-controlled storage, and it's only twenty dollars monthly if you pay six months up front. That's an average of three thousand dollars over the next ten years. Compared to having a larger basement built just to store it (and collect dust and add to my chores), interest, real estate taxes, and therapy, I was thousands of dollars ahead by storing these off-site.

3. ARCHIVE ARTICLES OF FAMILY HISTORY.

Do this for posterity. I suggest you get clean new boxes, line them with moth-proof bags (you can get them from the dry cleaner's), and place the articles inside. Be sure to label the boxes. As you know, I am wary of plastic containers, but in this case, Rubbermaid coffins are a good storage solution. Once you have repacked your treasures, place them in a clean corner of your attic or basement. Don't leave them in a to-do pile for decoupage projects from hell. It is enough to own them and keep them safe. Don't turn them into crap.

Among the more significant things that are passed on to us by our older relatives are holiday decorations. They ought to be stored properly in clean, solid containers that won't allow humidity, bugs, or mold to get inside. Do the Rubbermaid thing.

4. BE GENEROUS.

If you find that keeping Dad's train set is something that gets in the way of your leading an uncluttered life, consider passing it on to another family member. You're going a little bonkers with work and home, Dad's going to understand. If he doesn't, pass him on to another family member. You don't need the guilt. It is far better to give that train set to a responsible and interested younger niece or cousin than to hide it in a dusty, dark corner. The whole point of keeping something like this is to invoke family history. Better to keep it alive in the light than dead and buried in the dust.

5. SELL IT.

But for God's sake, don't be greedy. Getting money for your things can happen any number of ways. One is to consign them to a secondhand or antique store. Check around town for reputable ones, give them a call, and set something up. Some might buy things outright or will place them in their stores until they sell, at which time you get your money. Some dealers might come to your house to pick things up. A second way is to sell them yourself, a tag sale perhaps (for those of us who watch too much self-help television). But, please, don't drag out the process by listing your discarded treasures on an auction site like eBay. You'll open a whole other can of worms because you'll now be a shipper with tape, boxes, paper, packing, and bubble wrap. Don't do it! Pick out a good weekend, advertise, price, and put that sign up on your mailbox. As the day goes on and things don't seem to be moving, group them together and place a single price tag on specific lots. Don't forget to sell the junky tables you displayed the stuff on—people forget sometimes.

6. CALL GOODWILL OR A CHARITY SHOP.

Either will come out to your house and clean out your Holding Area. It's marvelous. In the case of Goodwill, they'll even give you a tax letter so you can claim a charitable donation on your taxes.

7. GO TO THE GODDAMNED DUMP.

Finally, haul it to your local dump. If what's left happens to be shoved into garbage cans, old laundry baskets, or other containers, leave them at the dump, too. You don't ever again want to have repositories for that much crap.

Jenny and I had us a big ol' tag sale. The television house-and-garden goddesses would have been proud. As Wes predicted, there was a stampede of salivating townies.

Allen O'Malley came by the day of the festivities. I nearly had a Hallmark moment and returned his scaffolding and air compressor, intending to thank him for spreading the bad rumors I suspected had initiated our recent good fortune. But he was accompanied by an obnoxious new client and I changed my mind. They were scrutinizing the house as though Jenny and I weren't even there.

"Can you believe that she-bastard?" I said, rushing to Jenny to get her attention.

"Leave it. Let it go," she said.

As I watched Allen and his sucker du jour, I fought the feeling that I was being expunged by Harbor Country. Chewed up and spit out.

"Stop staring at them," Jenny said. "It is a house sale. The house is empty. They're not seeing anything, really."

Sure they were. They were seeing the monument to my youthful aspirations. It hurt a little, as a matter of fact. I grew up in that house. Eighteen months earlier it would have made Style Network producers orgasm, charity house tour organizers flip, and passersby whisper, *You know what they say about big houses. Small dick.* Now it echoed, deserted, its architecture revealed for the vain effort at a world that existed in someone else's mind.

The sale was nearing the end and only a couple of card tables were left with sundry items strewn about. "Three bucks for these tables and what's on them!" I called out. "Three bucks!

"Keep your cheap shit!" a voice roared from a car with a gruff assortment of passengers driving away.

A wave of laughter washed over the remaining dozen or so people. Jenny, in particular, was laughing hysterically.

"Ah! Keep your fuckin' pants on!" I shouted back, taking ten cents on the dollar.

RESCUE EXERCISE

ARE YOU SUFFERING FROM NONESSENTIAL MADNESS?

1. Do you own platters for specific foods?

2. Do your slipcovers cost more than the chairs they cover?

3. Do you buy candlesticks for specific candles?

4. Exactly what do you do, and what do you buy, to "bring the outdoors in"?

5. Do you buy a pillow that causes you to rethink an entire room?

6. Are there books on your coffee table that you do not read regularly?

7. Do you buy oils and vinegars because you like how they look?

8. Do you frequently use the terms "focal point" and "area?"

9. Do you really believe that anything in a monthly Smith & Hawken catalogue is a new idea?

10. Do you have more vases in cabinets than you have out filled with flowers?

eighteen

Stanley Tigerman busied himself designing what he called "Thalido-mide Baby," our ode to camp on Georgetown Island. Predictably, I started giving him directions and tear sheets, not realizing that when you go to someone like Stanley Tigerman, you better give him the budget (have twice more saved), get out of his way, and let him do his stuff. Jenny, the voice of reason, put it this way: "One bedroom with a bathtub, and a small kitchen, please." He loved that.

Still, I was very self-conscious that I was, perhaps, out of my league. I'd never brushed shoulders with someone who had Michael Eisner's personal contact information. Jen was generally unfazed.

Wes called one day, dying to know what Stanley's fees were.

"Plenty," Jenny said.

I picked up the other phone. "I think I'm gonna have to ask him if he'll take postdated checks from a Discover card account," I joked.

"C'mon! How much damage can a twelve-hundred-square-foot house do?' Wes asked.

A chill ran down my spine when he said that. "Don't say that!" I said.

Wes laughed. "Honey, junk costs as much as the good stuff. I know. I design it!"

He was right. We knew from personal experience that it was very easy to spend as much on an architect of unremarkable skill as on one with international recognition. If it turned out to be a pile of crap it would be acclaimed crap, and this time not so big a heap.

Wes reported that skeptical Chicago Hamptonites were gossiping that we were very lucky to have sold the business at the price I negotiated. I wholeheartedly agreed.

"They paid a lot of money to wash dishes," I said.

While we waited out the house planning, Jenny did get a job baking cookies for some nice old Republicans at a swanky retirement home. Well, her official title was executive chef, but she told people she worked at a bakery.

And I started to work on my big screenplay.

I had decided many years before that it would be about old people who magically become young at Christmastime. Having been to L. L. Bean often enough, it seemed that it might be the perfect place to set it. Plus, I got caught up in an emerging notion of the simple life in Maine, which involved, oddly enough, working a hassle-free nine to five job at a socially conscious company. I went to Bean's and filled out an application.

"Don't you think you might be just a little overqualified to process returns?" Jenny asked when I announced the big offer.

"C'mon!" I begged. "Even Stuart didn't get this offer in the two years he searched."

The *Variety* front page flashed in my mind: "Olympian/Restaurateur/ Guamanian Writer Wins Oscar for Script about Old People."

"OK, here we go." Jenny saw the cameras rolling in my eyes. "He's baack."

I eagerly accepted my temporary holiday assignment at the L. L. Bean flagship retail store in Freeport, and straightaway became an unrecognizable, khaki-short-and-green-flannel-shirt-wearing customer support representative, a CSR. An elite member of retail's equivalent to the Navy SEALS, the cream of the crop. God, I was proud. Even the remote chance of someone from Harbor Country walking into the Customer Service Center to bust me in a bib apron and name tag making eleven dollars an hour didn't faze me. I drank the Kool-Aid.

I threw myself into the job with the same gusto I had shown in my previous adventures. In the back of my head I thought, These guys are gonna love me, they've never met anyone like me.

But I quickly discovered that I wasn't so special. I was but one of an army of individuals who were their own someone from someplace else who moved to Maine to escape their own rat races. I was stunned. All of us special somebodies, drawn to Freeport like my cousins to a free bucket of the Colonel's original-recipe chicken.

It was strangely thrilling to contemplate how L. L. Bean managed to turn all of us fancy people from someplace else into happy company people who, all of a sudden, hung out around time clocks. We were so happy. Two seconds out of training we went from describing ourselves in terms of our previous triumphs to openly seeking permanent hire positions with benefits like health insurance. We drugged ourselves with the hope that one day our lanyards would bear the coveted photo ID badge that wasn't stamped temporary across the front.

I grew ashamed to carry my temporary badge. It made me feel like I was underage, sub-par.

As a CSR, I happily supported L. L. Bean's world-famous Hundred Percent Satisfaction Guarantee, which was basically to accept anything that was returned. The age or condition of the article didn't matter so long as the customer was not completely satisfied. It didn't even matter if the return actually belonged to the customer (we were told that proof of purchase was not required) or if they had bought it at Goodwill. It was simply not the CSR's job to determine what satisfaction meant—rather, the customer defined satisfaction. Well, I knew exactly that kind of customer satisfaction intimately.

Meanwhile, Stuart was becoming civil. One day, he freely offered his municipal services when a small building problem popped up.

"I've asked the zoning codes enforcement officer to take a look at your electrical easement problem," he said, his voice odd in its accommodation.

The islands' building supervisors worked out of Phippsburg's town hall, where F&S held elected positions.

"Thanks, Stuart," I said, uncomfortably cheerful.

Jenny and I had rented a house in Georgetown while Stanley's Thalido-mide Baby was being built. Thus far, the only snafu had been this electrical easement issue.

Two weeks after he offered to flex his municipal muscle, Stuart brought us some news.

"Your neighbors will agree not to drive or park down the middle of your property," he reported, "if you split the cost of a new driveway and allow them to tie into your power pole for their own electricity line."

"Wow! That's it?" I said. "How much for the new driveway?"

"Five hundred. Less if you use the same guy who's going to dig your sep-tic," he said. "You'll get a package deal."

"That sounds like the situation we're looking for."

"The codes officer says that he's meeting Stanley next week to go over the expansion parameters for the boathouse."

"Yeah, the big man's coming out."

"Are you losing weight?" he said.

Actually, I was. I hadn't joined a gym or even begun what resembled an exercise regimen. I just walked and spent more time not working on the house doing I don't know what else. Maybe I was living.

"Stuart wants something!" I declared as Jenny walked in the door.

"Oh, yeah?"

"Three hours ago he asked me if I was losing weight," I said, flustered. "I was so floored that I asked him if he wanted anything at Bean's. He said he'd make me a list."

"I'm glad you two are making up," she said. "That would be nice for Fran-cesca and me."

The dogs barked wildly. Across the street, a group of three—what looked like parents and their teenage daughter—were digging for clams at the shore. Beatrice bayed long enough that I was readying myself for mouth to mouth. The thought made me shrink; her bloodhound's face was like a wet wheel of Saga blue cheese.

Stuart's car was at the end of the driveway, again.

"Everybody loves the guy with the L. L. Bean discount," I muttered.

STEP 4: IMPLEMENT

SETTLEMENT · *n.* **1** *the action or process of settling* **2** *an official agreement intended to resolve a dispute or conflict* **3** *a place in which people establish a community where previously there was none* **4** *law: an arrangement whereby property passes to a person or succession of people as dictated by the settlers* **5** *acceptance.*

nineteen

"Are you kidding me?" I said.

Jenny wasn't looking too happy.

"The thing about your electrical problem is that if you move the driveway and allow the neighbors to piggyback, the sellers will retract their deal with you, and Central Maine Power won't be able to run the lines."

I paused for a minute to absorb what Stuart had said.

"C'mon," Jenny said. "Electricity would seem to be an inalienable right!"

"There is no such thing as eminent domain in Maine," he replied. "He who owns the road says who can pass."

The old couple who sold us the property had granted us an easement over their property which would allow for electricity to be brought to our building site. What we were now finding out was that they were absolutely against the very same easement providing electricity to the other neighbor against whom they had waged a long-standing war over property rights. It sounded exactly like the same, inhospitable sense of entitlement Stuart and Francesca kept alive on their mosquito breeding grounds.

Yet somehow I wasn't worried. In my recent life, I would have grabbed the nearest ax and run into battle. But I had changed, in a quiet, sudden way. Intellectually, I knew that legal matters were always workable. At any rate, I couldn't imagine anyone saying no to the Tigerman.

Stanley had scheduled an on-site visit in a few days, partially to design the boathouse and also to interview construction companies. When Stuart offered to work with Central Maine Power and keep Stanley posted, it made sense to me why he was being so nice.

"He wants us to make him project manager," I whispered to Jenny as Stuart backed out of the driveway. She maintained that he only wanted to get to know Stanley. Either way, I was subdued.

At the happy Customer Service Center, I overheard a rare, sarcastic comment along the old catalogue bank.

"Is this why I graduated from MIT?" a voice muttered. "To defend this stupid fucking guarantee?"

I was flanked by two CSRs on that shift. The guy to my left made the comment. His name was Tom.

"What did you study?" Gretchen, the woman to my right, asked him.

"Nuclear physics," he replied. "I'm defending my dissertation any day now."

Well I could hardly believe what I had just heard. In fact, I ducked for fear that others heard it. No one spoke that way about beloved Bean's, yet there I was sandwiched between two *traitors*. Didn't they know The Guarantee secured their jobs, and therefore their dreams at brushing the permanent status brow? Didn't higher education teach Tom anything good? I confidently suggested that he might soon be working on the latest technology for the Maine hunting boot.

"I'm sure Bean's realizes what an asset you are!" I said brightly.

"I asked at Human Resources," he replied.

"Really? Were they helpful? I was thinking of giving them my resumé, actually."

"Forget it," Gretchen said. "I used to do the flowers for the Four Seasons New York. I answered an ad they placed here ten years ago for a permanent position in merchandising. Here I am, still seasonal temporary. No health insurance. Instead they hired some granola bitch who thinks a dead Christmas tree is a spring bouquet."

I cleared my throat and looked back at my customer, suggesting by the way I apologetically tilted my head that it might take me a while to find the product code for her shredded pair of snowshoes circa 1965.

"LK8529," Gretchen said, "your snowshoes. LK8529, eighty bucks, ten at the employee store."

"Thanks!" I said, amazed that she knew the product code. I started for my register, my head held high like a public television supporter who wore wool clogs. Mine were blue with Nordic embroidery.

"Why do you think the customer service here is so great?" Gretchen sneered, moving closer. "We're all such fucking professionals."

If, for a blissful moment, I imagined L. L. Bean as a retail version of Communist China; its president the Chairman Mao of Freeport, its CSRs happy, red-cheeked workers, I could not now ignore the plight of the people. I could easily succumb to this anti-Bean rhetoric, and Gretchen would be the one to facilitate it. She'd flipped a switch.

I smiled politely and returned to my customer, trying hard to be diligent in my heart. But I found that difficult when standing between Gretchen and Tom. My thoughts wandered while on shift and instead of dutifully stalking unsuspecting customers with an ever-ready big, happy smile, I sinfully remembered that I had two Viagra pills that I had blackmailed from David Rose for his misguided Depakote prescription. A chill ran down my loins.

The next week in the lunchroom I intended to have a company-faithful discussion with Tom and Gretchen. This time, my truancy was detectable. "So what's going on?" I asked them, knowing full well what they were talking about. It was the same thing everyone talked about..

"Nothing's going on, Dan," Gretchen said. "It's just the way it is."

"It's just so obvious," Tom replied, "that if you have a college degree or higher, they like to put you on the floor in Customer Service and *leave you there.*"

"It's a way for them to ensure quality service when people return the beds their dogs die in," Gretchen said.

I shushed them.

"Who gets the good jobs then?" I whispered.

"Old people," Gretchen deadpanned. "They're the ones getting the entry-level management positions."

At that moment, an elderly regular full-time CSR with whom I had exchanged greetings a couple of times walked by. I noticed a long scar up the side of his leg and recalled that he said he was "opened up" (for bypass surgery) on his sixty-eighth birthday.

I wavered slightly and felt guilty for being rebellious. "What if the old people have degrees?" I snickered, with some regret.

"DENTAL INSURANCE!" answered the two in aha! unison.

I went home and lay in bed to ponder this information. I found that I too was becoming somewhat disillusioned. Was L. L. Bean exploiting the hitherto unexploitable classes? How long had they chewed up and spit out people with good work histories and good skills who only wanted to move to Maine for a better life? I jotted all this down on a notepad I had titled "Bean's at Midnight." I wondered if L. L. Bean management was consciously aware that they tricked people like me, people with a dream of the perfect, simple life in Maine that included a forty-hour workweek among fleece and flannel.

"Any word from Stuart or Stanley regarding the power?" I asked Jenny over dinner.

"Nothing yet," she said tentatively.

"No news is good news, right?"

"Yeah, but I can't believe you haven't noticed anything."

I stopped and looked around. Everything seemed in place. She still looked good to me. Nothing new. "What?" I said.

"It's Friday night."

"Yes it is, dear, so—"

"So nothing," she said happily. "We're just sitting down. . . having dinner. . . on a Friday. . . *night*."

The dogs barked crazily again and we thought we saw our first moose. We spent the weekend stalking it, but it was only a piece of driftwood at high tide.

The old people at Bean's weren't like the ones in *Cocoon*. They were more like Stuart, unpredictable and aloof, except they were wrinkled and had all their natural teeth. They were nice enough on the floor to customers, legendary in terms of service, but in the lunchroom they were standoffish and private. No fuzzy grandfolks at L. L. Bean—instead, they were seventy-year-old snowboarders who said things like, "Dude, if you dropped some weight you could pick up a board with your forty percent discount before your assignment ends."

Dude? They were screwing up my screenplay.

The power easement issue became a longer than planned delay. Stanley and three months came and went. The sketches for the boathouse arrived depicting it as a watery screened porch. We looked forward to the groundbreaking of our noble little lunch box.

Meanwhile, I was struggling with a treatment for my script, in constant conflict with the stock characters in my head and the old characters at work. I fished Tom and Gretchen for material and grew sarcastic. Then one day I looked at Jenny's bill pile and realized my monthly insurance coverage was $738. Refusing to maintain that monthly bill, if I could help it, and, in my own way, demanding reasonable compensation for the forty hours I was putting in at fleece central, I submitted my résumé three times to Human Resources. Once for corporate banquet manager, another time for foodstuffs buyer, the third time for a position with L. L. Bean Home. As usual, my submissions went without acknowledgement.

One day at noon, Tom and Gretchen eyed the lunch Jenny had packed me.

"What's today's creation?" Tom asked hopefully.

"Looks like brown rice, sea bass she did Thai style, simple salad, and that's it." I offered to share it with both of them and they eagerly accepted. Gretchen offered me her PBJ but I declined.

"I wouldn't eat it either," she said, flipping it over her wrist.

We'd all applied for the same three jobs. Gretchen seethed.

"Not so much as a photocopied slip saying—"

"Fuck you very much?" I said.

"Exactly," Tom replied.

Last century's autumn became this century's first winter. Jenny and I, now nearly ten years together, spent the chilly days walking on beaches and through marshes, laughing as our dogs barked happily. Our bodies ached new pains—old occupational knots gave way to hikers' knees and stiff shoulders dulled by backpacks. Weekends arrived without dread and we threw ourselves into Friday nights without worries of editing wine lists, daily specials cards, and sober dishwashing staffs. We ate leisurely lunches that someone else had cooked, peeping, bite by bite at hot new affairs between new chefs, new products, and fresh takes at-not-so-new ideas. Now someone else was reducing the veal stock. Jenny explored her less pressured days by becoming the other women she was capable of becoming. I was readied myself for everything Dan Ho was destined to become.

Christmas week, one morning...

An old flannel shirt that didn't have an L. L. Bean tag crossed my counter and I decided, at first glance, that it was Eddie Bauer. My supervisor, Edna, had just returned from a hip-replacement operation so I opted not to call her. I did so knowing refusals were not to be made by CSRs without a team leader present. I spent a longer than normal time at the catalogue bank, searching for the product code, working up my nerve to free-agent.

It turned out to be a Bean shirt.

Edna hobbled by and physically escorted me back to my register. "I'm sorry, sir," she told the customer. "We're not usually this slow when looking up product codes."

The intervention was tantamount to being picked up for live organ donation in China. I'd been busted, apparently caught on camera. I'd forgotten about them. Edna gave me a pained smile and a series of quick, wobbly nods. Then she hobbled behind the steel door where the hand sanitizer was kept.

"Well, you can forget even getting an interview for permanent placement," Tom declared at lunch.

Gretchen wasn't so delicate. "Never mind even being asked back for the fucking summer third shift."

After lunch....

I was standing in my khaki shorts, eyeing a pair of teenaged girlfriends with multiple piercings and high platform shoes who were standing in the queue, fiddling with a backpack. Tom, Gretchen, and I exchanged looks and we proceeded to alternate stalling and speeding up transactions to avoid the pair. I was processing a return for moccasins that were unsatisfactory because the wool lining had ripped off the customer's toenail. He left it in the lining to prove his point.

I wasn't slow or fast enough. Unlike Gretchen, I hadn't committed twenty thousand product codes to memory.

The backpack now before me stank so badly my eyes burned. Yet I continued smiling. I was right under the black bubble and the girls were eager to process their return.

"I'd like to return this, please. I'm DISSATISFIED," declared the blonde.

She lowered her eyelids and stuck her chin out to demonstrate how dissatisfied she really was. Her friend, whose hair was laced with Kool-Aid-magenta streaks, folded her arms and went *humpf*. Her bottom front tooth was missing. Her tongue barbell slipped through the gap.

"Go for it," a voice hissed. I looked up. It was Gretchen.

"How exactly did this product fail to meet your expectations?" I asked, reaching capably for a blank three-ply return slip.

"Uh, hello? It's, like, blue," replied the blonde. "It's, like, stinky, too."

I tapped my pen. The front page of *Variety* flashed in my mind: "Guamanian Writer Wins Oscar for Nell-meets-Clueless Script."

"Like, Caitlin?!" chirped Pink. "When, like, did your backpack get so stinky?"

"Ahh!" a low voice moaned. It belonged to Tom who watched, mouth agape, while pushing a Next Line Please acrylic sign in front of him as his customer left.

For Tom and Gretchen, this was my Norma Rae moment. They covered my back by going into the low cough mode which signaled Edna at fifty paces.

These girls picked the wrong CSR.

I cleared my throat.

"I'm sure that when you received this backpack," I said defiantly, "you received it first qua—"

Suddenly the stench was unbearable. "Quality" came out "*quaba-ha-haba-hality.*"

"Caitlin? Hello!" squeaked Pink. "Like, your book pack wasn't always so stinky? When did it get so stinky?"

Caitlin shifted impatiently. "Like, I don't know, Amber, like, I think it got stinky in the last, like, week."

"Can I just, like, get my money back? Like today?" Amber asked squarely.

My eyes burned and I blinked in quick succession. Gretchen was doing the wave.

"Like, it's skanky, dude, c'mon!"

I reached out to unzip the bag per Product Failure Survey Protocol and flipped over the main pouch. In it was a mass of unidentifiable slime, something of a very bad provenance.

"Like, oh my God, Caitlin, is that, like, what I think it is?"

"Buah, uh, do you have a deceipt?" I gagged.

"Like, hello, Amber? How would I know?"

Everything. Slowed. Down. My perception of fast and slow got mixed up.

Caitlin rebuked Amber with flailing wrists. Amber responded by turning the barbell between her teeth. I gulped silently, unsure if I could continue the conversation in English.

"When exactly did, like, your backpack get so stinky, dude? It wasn't me—"

"Like, I don't know, Amber, all right? I think it was like winter preowm."

Prom? I wasn't seeing the *Variety* headline in my head anymore. Now it was Dan Rather with a shocking story on 48 Hours.

"I'm going to have to speak to my *woofpervisor* about this," I said, twitching. "Would you excuse me, pwease?" And then, without warning, I broke into incoherent native babble. *"Kalakas, Kalakas, Kalakas!!"*

"EBDA! EBDA!" I screamed, suddenly so completely bilingual but barely able to get behind the steel doors fast enough. I wanted to sanitize my hands desperately but I was afraid to let go for fear of having to touch it again.

"HEY! HEY! HAAYY!" Edna screeched.

She appeared from a haze of fluorescent light, trying to tuck a half-eaten Nestlé Crunch bar into her apron.

"What the HELL is your problem?"

I knew that she had been monitoring me. Her eyes popped out like security bubbles between her webby wrinkled lids.

"SIDDOWN!" she cackled through chocolate teeth.

I motioned nervously to the backpack in my hand. A yeasty foam rose from my stomach and I felt a cold sweat.

"WELL WHAT'S WRONG WITH IT, MAN?" she said.

"It's *bwoo, lanyakalakaskalakas!!!!*"

"Massholes!"

Edna grabbed the bag with both hands. She pried open the flaps and stuck her nose and mouth in it.

"FOR ONE THING, IT SMELLS LIKE SHIT!" she said, pulling the bag away, her tone gruesome and instructional.

She gathered the flaps between her thumbs and forefingers so she could turn it inside out. And that's when I started to gag.

"WHAT IN THE GODDAMNED HELL IS THE MATTER WITH YOU?" she yelled.

"*Hagababahabagahagaba...*"

"WHAT?" she demanded.

The tips of her fingers were smeared with the suspect matter inside the backpack, which required me to check my breathing.

"*Pwease, nevermimeba.*"

I steadied myself on a bald spot on her eyelid. She blinked and it seemed as though that eyeball never got covered.

I held a deep, defiant breath and gazed up for what seemed forever. When I focused on Edna again she looked really old. In an instant, her voice had changed. Now she sounded like an old moose cow.

"And you temporaries think you got what it takes to be permanent," she lowed. "Drown my kitty cats, all of you wannabes, if you could. That's what greed and jealousy does."

My neck ached from the stress, my head from the insults, my butt cheeks from the clenching. My eyes wandered to the ceiling behind her, to a far corner of the wing that routed returns to the employee store. A ceiling fan spun dutifully. I recognized its rhythm and appreciated its comforting, cool breeze.

I apologized to the girls for having taken so long to process the return. Edna ordered me to blue bag the back pack for resale in the employee store. Per the company's Do What It Takes Clause, I processed Caitlin's return and gave her a goddamned kayak.

"BASTARD!" saluted Tom and Gretchen gleefully. "Represents!" I drowned some Bean kitty cat, alright. Right up its polar fleeced ass.

My assignment ended New Year's Day. I spent my paycheck and final discount opportunities on two sets of snowshoes and monogrammed dog beds. Then I took my fancy background and Tigerman-designed ass home.

For days after that, I sat staring at my computer, unable even to imagine the opening scene of *Beans at Christmastime.*

Only up to go from here was really all I could manage to type.

twenty

A sacred complex appropriated to vulgar use.

Like spongy morels in a damp, sandy springtime, six little structures slightly tall for their size grew from a clearing that tumbled into the bay, connected to each other as if by Popsicle sticks arranged by Keebler elves, or perfectionist tunnel-visioned Scandinavians.

The main structure measured only 20x40 feet, though it had a story and a half. There was no basement, only a crawl space for mechanical equipment. You entered it via pocket doors in a connected bump-out with a stairwell and half bath to the left, and a doorway to the kitchen to the right. You walked through the kitchen to a dining room immediately beyond it and, at the far end, twin cubed alcoves for built-in sofas. A three-foot aisle ran throughout the length.

At the top of the stairs was a landing with twin cubes on either side above the kitchen. It became a steel and glass bridge that informed the aisle below, passing over the dining table and terminating at a door between twin cubes above the sofa alcoves. A full bath was the left cube, and a closet, the right.

An eight-sided auxiliary structure, only 16-x-16 feet, was attached to the end of the main structure by a four-foot covered breezeway. Downstairs, beyond the sofa alcoves was a living room with a concrete fireplace. Above it, on the other side of the door at the end of the steel and glass bridge, was our bedroom, in it a soaking tub with a view of the bay.

Connected by a simple wood walkway, a 10-x-10-foot screened-in hut sat on a small bluff overlooking the water. It had a simple shower with a sunflower spigot.

Below it, where water lapped at its pilings, the rebuilt boathouse became another, slightly longer screened-in hut, connected to the other on the bluff by a wooden staircase and bridge.

At the end of the driveway a Lilliputian 8-x-4-foot utility house was constructed of the same material for odds and ends like shovels, hoses, and snowshoes.

Interior finishes were not painted: The kitchen cabinets, walls, and ceilings were a clear birch. White Corian and butcher block were the counter surfaces. Exposed silver dipped lightbulbs at the end of nondescript housing lit the dwelling throughout.

The exterior materials were corrugated aluminum and tough, marine-grade wood sheeting painted bright white with boat paint. Stanley liked the combination of white and metal against nature. He said it made nature look good.

No landscaping except for a simple aggregate driveway and a small 9-x-9-foot garden grid attached to the bump-out. A large stone fire pit was dug out by the screened hut.

The total square footage, including the huts, was under sixteen hundred feet.

Eight months earlier, Jenny and I had quickly agreed to the neighbors' offer to move their driveway. It had just now been completed. The approach was ours. The package deal included a septic field and resurfacing for water runoff, which were installed right away.

Stanley asked us if we had considered naming the house, as his clients often did. "It looks like a little white church in the woods," Jenny said.

"Definitely," I agreed.

I suggested St. Homarus from the Latin for lobsters trapped in the bay.

We told Stanley we'd do two weeks of heraldry, but by the time we turned to more serious thoughts about the house, we'd been given the definitive thumbs-down on the matter of electricity. Central Maine Power was not going to run it. Period. This time we hired a lawyer. As I was signing the retainer check, I considered the date. 3/12/2000. It had been twenty-five months since my seizure. The setting sun cast shadows behind the cardboard trees on the precise scale model of Stanley's Thalidomide Baby.

Jenny and I accepted that we would definitely not be moving into the Tigerman anytime soon, so we decided to get comfortable. The furniture in the leased house was not ours, and after nearly a year of being guests we gave in to our desire to set up our own place. We were without a home. We weren't quite ready to accept our entire load of goods from Michigan, so we went peeking into the off-site storage locker in Portland, the old salty port city forty minutes away.

"Can you remember the last time we ate breakfast in a different city and weren't taking notes for Jenny's?" I said over breakfast, trying to soften the blow dealt to us by the power company.

Earlier we had retrieved a couple of rugs and a chair and strapped them onto the top of the car. I eyed them through the storefront window of a tiny café, maybe eight tables, in the old downtown.

"Mmm, it's nice to have good pancakes," Jenny said, inspecting the crumb. "They folded in whipped egg whites."

I ate oatmeal and mentioned that it wasn't as good as St. Agony's.

"You were out of your mind," Jenny said.

"Not yet I wasn't."

Outside, pages of a city newspaper blew at our feet—personal ads. *Busty redhead in need of discipline,* one bold face rectangle blared; *extremely flexible mature non-smoking female,* said another. Over the next two months we returned repeatedly to the same spot for weekend breakfast and to cheer up. We were always stumbling or crunching over a stray poster or neighborhood bulletin. The gusts off Casco Bay blew fiercely and the dark old buildings sheltered winds that conspired to launch microbursts.

One day we walked from breakfast into a brick monstrosity—a museum—that displayed I. M. Pei's design plaque.

"He must have had an off day," I muttered to Jen when she discovered it quite to her surprise.

We peeked into its unremarkable gift shop, buying nothing, and later into an antique store or two, but only to look. Once we took in a $2 matinee at the run down Cinema and handed a homeless drunk a couple of bucks. The grandest hotel, The Eastland, had been newly purchased, the headlines read, but the lethargic new owners (so the breakfast crowd whispered) had yet to paint over the huge sign on its harbor side that screamed *Ramada Inn, best rates, free continental breakfast.*

Graffiti was sprayed about the town. Wrinkled adults passed them by apologetically, as though they were excusing the antics of their misbehaving children. Some had tried to wash them off, but conceded to their chemical permanence in an abandoned effort now frozen in diluted, petrified streaks.

It didn't take long for us to reason that while our new home in Georgetown was being built, and since we were renting anyway, we ought to move into the city for a while and immerse ourselves in its emerging charms. At least we could enjoy the outdoors without dodging mosquitoes and blackflies.

We looked for apartments but to no avail. There wasn't one that would take Beatrice and Ada.

The real estate agent called late one afternoon. Finally, something had opened up. "The landlord pays the heat," he said assuredly, deferring so that we entered first.

The place smelled like that free heat was from burning dung. It was a shabby, nicotine-stained three-bedroom sauna, with industrial brown carpeting, drop ceilings, and peeling lead paint in a building with seven other units. The lobby hinted wearily at *The Age of Innocence,* but the lucrative temptations of slumlording, and the economic crash of the late eighties in New England had determined what seemed to be an irreversible state of decline.

"Stanley would shit a green worm," I said to Jenny as we waved the real estate agent good-bye and night fell on the street before the imposingly pathetic apartment building.

A real live punk rocker stumbled down the stairs in a kilt and leather jacket. A car horn sounded ten feet from where we stood and a pit bull lunged at a rear window. The punk rocker skipped to the driver's seat and got in, but not before the driver wrestled, sometimes not so successfully, with the dog. I hurried Jenny a few steps to the big Ramada Inn sign. The hotel had a rooftop bar. As we waited to cross at the corner I looked up at the street sign. -eerie- street. Someone had spray-painted over the first and last letters.

"It probably rotates," Jenny said, referring to the bar. She grimaced at the pervasive smell of stale cigarettes extinguished in beer that wafted throughout the hotel.

But the drinks were cheap and the view, spectacular.

"Jesus, Jen, look at that."

I pointed to a torn section of a tar roof twelve stories below on Eerie Street. Peeking through it was a mass of garbage and feathers, probably a pigeon tenement. A gigantic, tattered white bra lay next to it in symbolic neglect. "I think that's the building we looked at."

It's true about strikes—they happen in threes. I failed at being happy in Michigan. I failed at keeping an eleven-dollar-an-hour job in Freeport. Now I had failed to set up house on Georgetown Island. Strange how I still felt that the third time was the charm. Third time for what? A new place to live was attempt number four at happiness. I was out of the luck loop.

The power easement situation soon ground to a complete halt, despite my best efforts. And then our landlord decided not to renew us because he'd gotten an offer from a *real* Hamptonite for big money for the whole summer. There wasn't an available *livable* apartment in Portland that would accommodate us, no matter how simple we'd become and how complicated the search effort. In an uncomfortable though recently familiar desperation, we bought the building on Eerie Street before the hard-working real estate agent put the for sale sign up.

Stuart was quick with his nauseating, experienced brownstonian know-how. That was enough for me to tackle it straight on with dogged, alienating valor.

With the assistance of a capable, slow, but expensive carpenter, tradesmen, and twelve-hour nondrowsy Sudafeds, we blasted out three of the first-floor apartments and created our new two-bedroom, one-and-a-half bath, thirteen-hundred-square-foot home in old downtown Portland. I poured into it every lesson I'd gleaned from my Rescue, and the expensive Tigerman education. Except that this was all done in the context of restoring nearly century-and-a-half-old plaster acanthus leaves and massive mahogany doors. It was a Rescue within a Rescue.

"You know, there's a trick to tenants," Stuart said, picking over the architecture of the four apartments on the second and third floors. "You don't just learn this stuff overnight."

"Jenny!" Francesca chirped. "It's beeee-autiful!"

The structure was built in 1868 by a ship's captain, back in the day when the first floor of homes were meant to impress. (Times have changed, haven't they? These days our crappers are the showplaces.) To our great relief, it retained original features hidden under what turned out to be painful though reversible conditions. The house was narrow, and the rooms stacked linearly so our New Pantry and New Walk-In ended up being tucked away in old hallways that the improvement rendered useless. Actually, Stanley's philosophies translated well to the compartmentalized Victorian architecture already in place.

Instead of building a house, we took part of a big house—so big, in fact, that we ended up selling off the top floors—and made it our own. I couldn't bear to tell Stuart that I wasn't cut out to be a landlord.

Finally, in early 2001 we were home. The drywall dust was gone. All the furniture that survived the Michigan Rescue was in place. The Christmas ornaments, packaged in Rubbermaid coffins, were stored only four blocks away, along with other, important nonessentials. Jenny got her bathtub in the bedroom and surrounded it with orchids and strangely shaped succulents, always a secret passion of hers but she had never had the time. Now she did. We trotted to the farmer's market every other day. I got rid of my car and with the dogs walked everywhere. They got more exercise in the city on leashes than they had in their enclosed two-acre artery-blocking park in Harbor Country. As a matter of fact, so did I. I lost 50 pounds just from walking around town. When my thighs had shrunk, and nothing else did, I knew then that the old port city was growing on us. And I accepted that I would probably never be a writer of any consequence, at least not any time soon. Portland had become home.

I lobbied for the condo members on the third floor to hire our carpenter, Brian, to construct their swanky pied-à-terre. The phone rang as I sat quietly making secret notes for a cookbook. I could hear Brian's voice clearly when Jen picked up the phone.

"Why don't you two come up and see the replacement windows I've put in on the third floor?" he said.

Jenny was intrigued and went up. I wasn't interested in reliving Brian's slow, painful, brilliant processes so I stayed behind. After nearly a decade dealing with construction, I was officially on sabbatical. There were times when I thought I'd have to call David Rose and beg for a tranquilizer prescription while waiting for Brian to come to a decision about a sixteenth of an inch. Toward the end of our remodeling I had become irritable. I still couldn't have a conversation with him without feeling deeply guilty about having chewed his head off a couple of times. In truth, I was much more calm and diplomatic than I had ever been in my life. Still, I didn't like feeling that desparate for perfection and vowed never to go there ever again.

Jenny returned a few minutes later.

"Well?" I asked. "What's up with the replacement windows?"

"They really make a difference, Dan. They're really tight." She looked hopeful and I became alarmed.

"Yeah, but how do they look?" I said.

We'd spent much time discussing the merits of old glass. I was dreading having to do it again.

"Ugly, but Brian reports that they'll pay for themselves in the first year," she said in a *maybe we should do it like he suggested in the first place* way.

I jumped up and added our heating bills, divided that total by the number of condo members (three), and reported quickly back to Jenny that the annual expense was roughly one thousand dollars. I couldn't see how Brian's purported savings could be true. She convinced me to have a look anyway.

The windows were, in fact, hideous. Airtight but hideous, suffocating in their unsightliness. She asked me for my opinion.

I went into an incoherent babble that included, *We bought an 1868 house..*
.Damn it...It's valuable because of its age and integrity...What the hell...It was
built before insulation...You want airtight?...Why don't we just live in an SUV
and park it in Georgetown?...This is like a vintage convertible...Why would
you put a new windshield on a vintage car?...The Victorians solved their win-
dow draft problems with drapes...Don't tell me you're going to put us through
more remodeling...Why don't we get drapes instead?

"Your writer's block is getting to be insufferable," she said. "Brian said
that the new sashes would last forever."

She'd said it, the F-word.

I'd become weary of the historical preservationists suggesting that although the city allowed steel, we should replace the old copper gutters with
new copper gutters—custom-made at a ridiculous price that took forever to
fabricate. "Copper lasts forever" didn't fly with me because, shit, if it did,
why the hell were we replacing it?

"Don't you ever talk about *forever* with me."

"Oh, go think of a movie, will you?" she said.

We went to bed without saying anything, backs to each other. I spent the
night close to the edge, the side closest to the radiator.

In the morning, I took the dogs for a walk and ran into Brian, who com-
mented that it was cold. "You guys gonna get replacement windows?" he
asked.

Pissed off, with a stiff neck, I looked him up and down, the way the neck-
braced Joan Collins did on Dynasty after she and Linda Evans bitch-slapped
each other.

"You know why I left Guam, don't you?" I said.

"Because you got a job with the Ice Capades?"

"Because it was fucking HOT!" I said stiffly.

"Well, then," he quipped, "you're gonna love it in Portland."

The dogs and I walked to Deering Oaks Park, a barely maintained though
cherished oasis designed by Frederick Law Olmsted. I watched skaters on
the frozen pond while the dogs chased each other—they were happy in the

park. Our girls are beautiful. Ada looks like Christy Turlington. Bea looks like Sandra Bullock and sings like Barry White.

I thought about how much Jen and I worked like dogs, how smart we were, how sleepless we were, and how now we didn't need to worry about a couple hundred lousy dollars for heat if that meant enjoying the swirls of old Victorian glass. What was next? I thought of all the rehab and remodel shows choking the airwaves. Even the local alternative newspaper, advertising wanton sex requests, featured advertising bubbles that read "as seen on HGTV" on the very same pages as classifieds by divorced men and granny trannies. We were Rescued now. I didn't want to end up one of those people who washed out their Ziplock bags, leaving them to dry upside down on their pissy-ass Kohler faucets.

Crap loomed again. As we walked past the skating rink, I remembered that for three seasons it was a lagoon with a spectacular fountain. Three out of four seasons replacement windows were irrelevant. I was different. Our real life with old windows was perfectly gorgeous. There would be no more home improvement. I would pursue something more important: Homeowner—my own— improvement.

The girls and I returned from our walk and found that Jenny's car was gone. In its place was Stuart's Swedish car, with their new yellow Lab puppy in the back on an L. L. Bean cedar-filled bed. I wanted to puke. Brian had concluded giving Stuart a tour of the building when the three of us met in the driveway.

"Brian tells me you're seriously considering *not* replacing these old windows," Stuart said. I shot Brian a look that reminded him he needed to run to Home Depot very quickly.

I invited Stuart in for coffee. After seeing Jen's note that she'd be right back. I figured I could pass him on and wander into town pretending to be on a recipe fact-finding mission.

"I'd listen to Brian if I were you, Dan," said Stuart. "He knows what he's doing. Do you know what an R-rating differential is?"

I noticed Stuart must have lost a cap on his front tooth and *that* replacement wasn't a good color match. I stifled a smile. He said that his new construction loan was past due and they needed to roll it over into a mortgage. He needed a really fast carpenter and wondered about Brian. Of course I said Brian was the fastest carpenter I had ever met.

Perfect.

In June, Central Maine Power informed us that they had reconsidered and were ready to propose a way around the easement so we could get electricity. We called Stanley and told him that since we'd fallen in love with Portland, we didn't quite know what to do with the Thalidomide Baby.

"Do you have a screened porch in the city?" he asked.

We didn't.

"Fine," he said. "Forget all the crap in Georgetown. We'll just turn the place into a big screened porch. It's what I envisioned in the first place."

Yeah, really, screw minimalism. There are mosquitoes and blackflies to battle.

twenty-one

The dead of a New England winter, February 2001.

Wes sends me an e-mail: *No, as a Catholic male I never once believed that because Jesus died at 33, so would I. Is this what led you to deny the nauseating masses of Harbor Country their beloved Thai Style Chilean Sea Bass?*

I respond: *What a great idea! But no. It was something I wrote and stuck into the Holding Area for Emotions—you remember that exercise?*

Wes: *If you mean that plastic bucket that Garden hot glued silk peonies to, who could forget? Glad it got used for something. You know, Bill left me all the 90's furniture.*

Me: *Jen wants you to send her all your cookie sheets except the Teflon ones you bake pinecones on. When are you coming to Maine? There's a great hotel three doors away. It's just your thing. Très Gucci.*

Wes: *I'll come...but first tell me what to do with all this crap. It's all a bit overwhelming, this new life.*

Me: *Here's your advice, Mary. Hang in there.*

RESCUE RULE #1

MAKE YOUR HOME YOUR HOTEL SUITE

If you haven't stayed in a fancy hotel suite, go to your nearest nice hotel and tell the reservations desk that you're looking for a place to spend your wedding night. They'll show it to you. You should find a spacious allotment of two or three rooms, every square inch of which is designed for your ultimate comfort. It may or may not have a kitchen.

It most definitely will lack an extra unused bedroom, an attic, and a basement in which unused shit is piled. It won't have unnecessary bookcases to hold books you don't read. It won't have milk crates filled with old yoga tapes and dumbells that, for some inexplicable reason, you can't bring yourself to give to charity. It won't be filled with the crap we tend to hoard in search of the perfect movie scene. It'll be a complete, well-thought-out space.

If it isn't, then you're probably at the hotel near my house.

It should be a plush cocoon without being packed full of impulse, harmonious and lovely. It is a place you would love to call home if you didn't need to have a storage shed, basement, and attic to hold everything that gets in your way. A place to call home if you could afford it.

You can afford this setup. Go home, Assess, Analyze, and Improve, and then make your goal nothing less than creating a home in which you can feel like you're the star of your own movie, not the maid.

RESCUE RULE #2

OPEN BEFORE CHRISTMAS

Don't wait until special occasions to use your best things. Use them every day, and discard the so-so items you reduce yourself to using when the guests aren't looking. Rid yourself of the sick notion that you have everyday dishes and good china. Fuck it, eat cornflakes in your best bowl with your best spoon. Stop just displaying your pretty things. Put Saran Wrap around a Limoges plate holding leftover pork chops and stick it in the fridge. Why are you putting your leftovers in beat-up, yellowing Tupperware or blurry excuses for plastic bags that no longer zip or lock?

Stop the good stuff/everyday stuff charade; people despise martyrs. We come by our home lives honestly if we don't lift them from HGTV or magazines. Who the hell do you think you're fooling? Do your guests (more important, do you) really believe you're Marie Antoinette because you use Grande Baroque silver at Easter? Or that you're doing, in Northbrook, Illinois, what M. F. K. Fisher did when she was drunk on Lillet in the Loire Valley? If we spend our days eating on paper plates and then suddenly we eat on fine porcelain simply for the sake of showing off, our interactions become dishonest.

You are not being hospitable and generous to your guests by polishing silverware you shun as part of your daily existence. When you invite guests into your home, you ask them to partake of what's inside you, not make-believe. You can always send them food and a subscription to Domestic Goddess Monthly and spare yourself the trouble and expense.

We are awkward when we use new things. Make your best things your old things. Get comfortable with them so that you can be more generous to yourself and those who participate in your life.

RESCUE RULE #3

YOU DON'T NEED MORE CLOSET SPACE

You have a dresser, yet find that you have no room for your clothes. Your first impulse is to go out and buy another dresser, right? Most of us just start dreaming of moving to a new house or apartment based solely on the misguided notion that closet space equals complete happiness.

Clothes fuck people up. You should consider getting rid of some of yours.

I have a rule I follow. Every time I buy one item of clothing, I get rid of a similar item. If I buy a pair of jeans, I get rid of a pair of jeans. If I buy a sweater, I'll get rid of an old one. I follow this rule right down to my socks. I know people who think clothes are an investment, and their clothes-accumulation pattern spills over to the rest of their lives. Clothes are necessary, this is true, but only the same way toilet paper and toothpaste are—they are disposable.

So cull, cull, cull, and fold like you work at the Gap.

RESCUE RULE #4

BEWARE THE CRAFT PROJECT

Do not buy that glue gun unless you are going into the wholesale craft business with annual sales of over a quarter of a million dollars. Don't buy the power drill if you only have a few screws to tighten. Do not start collecting kits (like soap and candle making) just to give cute gifts.

Stop yourself from collecting ribbons at tag sales just because you saw someone else do it. Are you that prolific a gift giver? Do you, and do you think others ought to judge you, based on gift wrapping? Do you judge them on that basis? Why are you appropriating time, resources, and space for dried wreath supplies when you can buy a great one for less on a pleasurable trip? Ai, yi, yi.

Speaking of wreaths, a good way to keep your crap in check is to ask yourself, *When I die, and my friends and relatives are cleaning out my house, will they say, What the hell is all this crap?*

RESCUE RULE #5

BEWARE OF FOOD

Do not buy a lot of anything just because it's cheap, especially food. If you load up at Sam's Club, you are probably always looking for something fresh to cook. Why? Because all that stuff you buy in boatloads you've had to throw into the freezer. No one is keen on eating the same thing every day. Your freezer is full, but you have no inspirations. Bulk buying makes for boring, unfresh meals.

Eat fresher food by buying less food. Make small, sane shopping trips, instead of going on stressed-out sprees. Stop wondering why you don't have time to go to the gym three times a week and walk to the grocery store three times a week instead. You can walk, you know, especially if you don't need a Lincoln Navigator to haul the inventory home.

Distinguish for yourself the difference between concoction and ingredient. Concoctions are things like Chipotle Pepper Orange Marmalade, Roasted Garlic and Three Peppercorn Olive Oil, frozen margarita mix. These are one trick-ponies. They are not versatile. They make horrible gifts and even worse pantry items.

Ingredients are white vinegar, salt, sugar, oil, vodka, and Cointreau. Mix them together when you need to and don't buy into this infused and pan-fusion culinary bullshit that everyone is hawking. Don't buy the entire set of test tubes of spices just to put out on the counter. Buy a savings bond instead, and obtain the needed amount of fresh spices at your local co-op.

RESCUE RULE #6

GET OUT OF THE HOUSE

Do it! Just leave and find something else to do off-site. I frighten myself when I think of what my expectations were of our house in Michigan— that it had to be everything. A resort (pool, deck, and custom grill); a cottage (screened porch overlooking the roses), the country (large lawn), and the showcase. It couldn't be just a safe, comfortable place for when the workday was over.

We become narrow-minded as we pursue the completely outfitted home. Hey! Spas all over the world have better pools than we can ever afford to build, so go to them. I tried in vain to recreate a garden I saw in England. With the amount of money I spent on that attempt, I could have returned to England for years and years to enjoy it, as well as other gardens (in Tuscany, Paris, and The Hague). I spent (and you do, too) too much time mustering the energy to curse swarms of Japanese beetles from my tea hybrids. We can enjoy infinitely more flora for less money.

RESCUE SUMMARY

NO MORE CRAP

We can allow ourselves gardens, pools, and other nice things. But our homes need to be havens with reasonable maintenance requirements so that they are restful. The chores before the styling chores are challenging enough. Piling our energy into a series of tableaux that have no lasting value except to satisfy a fleeting visual fix is a doomed enterprise.

We cannot expect our homes to thrill every one of our senses. If we start on that path we lose. We deny ourselves the opportunity to encounter ourselves in the larger world. Look around. People are putting Versailles in their backyards. They're buying Hummers to brave the inhospitable suburban terrain. We're not any more serene or efficient for any of it.

Don't own a park, go to the park. Don't make that expensive remodel so the kids have a room in which to isolate themselves, teach them what else exists beyond the drywall. Don't believe for one minute that if you build the dream home, that the dream life follows. Understand that true style is choice, and life, in all its glorious imperfections, is the absolute arbiter of personal style.

A couple of weeks later, Wes sends me an AOL buddy message:

You there? The movers came today. Maybe I should rent a studio and make this place my Holding Area for life. So are you writing a movie, your will (again) or what?

Me: *Screenplay failed. Fuckin' old people in Maine. They all work at LL Bean and rock climb in the nude. Who the hell wants to see that on the big screen?*

Wes: *Cookbook!!!!!!!!!!*

epilogue

One morning Jenny says to me as we wake up, "Dan, you're no fun any-more, dreaming of the next cake bible. Why don't you just write what you know?"

"What's that?" I ask sleepily.

"Food! Food you like to eat—food you know people like to eat. Just write a cookbook of simple, time-tested recipes Americans enjoy."

"Yuck. Like we need another three hundred pages on how to boil pasta *al dente*."

"Your choice," she says, "but that's what publishers publish."

I agree in a low waking tone.

"I'll even help."

We get up and take the dogs out for their walk. When we return, Jenny gets ready for work and whistles happily as she walks to her car. She is go-ing to turn in her vacation requests for four dates. A week with Wes, a long weekend with House, a leaf-peeping hike with Francesca and Samantha when the mosquitoes die, and five days at a spa, alone. She will go without me these times. A new and tentative thing for us, these individual vacations, but exciting and educational.

I myself have never spent so much time staring at a computer. Ah, the great afterlife.

The dogs and I watch from the porch as Jenny starts her car and backs up. She stops and rolls down the window.

"Did you forget something?" I call out, shivering.

"You really know food, you know," she says, leaning out her window.

"No, you really know food," I reply. "Go! You'll be late."

She smiles and calls out "Cookbook!" as she drives down our city street.

With pad in backpack, I walk around old Portland over newsprint slush, past bloodied seagulls arguing with dalmatian pigeons. I glance at a familiar unwashed face, woolly hair a faded blaze of red. A pint of whiskey is plump and new in her excited old hands with fingernails of shredded wheat. She reaches out, and I give her a dollar.

I find a new place where I sit and watch the oil barges, a restaurant that doesn't enjoy much business. Management has posted a Help Wanted sign, flexible hours with benefits. I envision a shiny new exhaust fan and walk-in, then shrug it off. The sheen of imagined steel blurs to a sloppy bottle of hot sauce.

Don't get distracted, I tell myself. For once in your life, do something regular.

So I take out my pad and pencil and start to write the cookbook. Here it is.

THE END